'This is the perfect book for those who want to understand the fog of those extraordinary years, and what happened when it lifted and things became visible again and clear to see; it is the perfect book for those who want to understand the clash between a generation that grew up surrounded by that fog and a generation that grew up without fog, needing and wanting to confront things as they are and not as we dreamed they might be; it is the perfect book for those who want to understand what it means, for millennials, to be their fathers' children. ... Many reviews of this very sophisticated, intense, historical and intimate book claim that it narrates "the loss of a father". I would say otherwise ... This is a book about paternity as a cleaving in two, and it is an unblinking account of what is to be gained by learning who our fathers really are – we free them from the yoke of our expectations and, in doing so, extinguish any form of debt or servitude'
Simonetta Sciandivasci, *Il Foglio*

Sunken City

Sunken City

MARTA BARONE

translated by Julia MacGibbon

First published in Great Britain in 2022 by
Serpent's Tail,
an imprint of PROFILE BOOKS LTD
29 Cloth Fair
London
EC1A 7JQ
www.serpentstail.com

Originally published in Italy in 2020 by Giunti Editore S.p.A./Bompiani
Copyright © 2020 Giunti Editore S.p.A./Bompiani, Firenze-Milano
www.giunti.it
www.bompiani.it

Translation copyright © Julia MacGibbon 2022
Chronology of Key Events © Julia MacGibbon 2022

This work has been translated with the contribution of the Centro per il libro e la lettura for the Italian Ministry of Culture.
Quest'opera è stata tradotta con il contributo del Centro per il libro e la lettura del Ministero della Cultura italiano.

CENTRO
PER IL LIBRO
E LA LETTURA

10 9 8 7 6 5 4 3 2 1

Typeset in Freight Text by MacGuru Ltd
Designed by Barneby Ltd
Printed and bound in Great Britain by Clays Ltd, Elcograf S.p.A.

A CIP record for this book can be obtained from the British Library

ISBN: 978 1 78816 855 7
eISBN: 978 1 78283 875 3

For the young man

Sunken City

'Of the whole man you're left / with a part of speech. Of speech, that is. A part of speech.'

Joseph Brodsky

'To turn down the Légion d'Honneur is not enough. One should never deserve it.'

Erik Satie

Martingale (ˈmɑːtɪnˌɡeɪl), n. Any gambling system in which the stakes are raised, usually doubled, after each loss

I

THE FIRST KITEZH

This story has two beginnings. At least two, because, as with everything in life, it is always hard to establish what begins and when, what whirl of fortuitous circumstances lies behind a seemingly unpredictable episode, or which face turned to look at another at some point in the past, setting in train the random chain of events and of beings that led to our existence. First of all – this I can say with some certainty – I was born. It was March and it was snowing, and the year was 1987. My parents had met just two years previously and would separate for good three years later.

I was born to a woman with a hole in her head. My mother had been in a road accident, thirteen years earlier. After my birth, I spent a week under observation because I was in withdrawal from the antiepileptic drugs she was still forced to take. Of the accident, the coma and the operations, there remained only a slight hollow at the spot where part of her skull was missing – replaced by a piece of metal mesh which, over time, had been masked by her fine, feather-light hair. She always lies on her other side to sleep, because the section of head she doesn't have continues to ache.

It could be said that, for good or ill, I sprang from that hole. My very existence depends on that wound, that open door on to the cliff edge of possibilities. When my mother, at the age of twenty, fell off a motorbike being driven by someone else, she was accompanying him to pick up the documents that would have allowed them to marry. That's not the way things turned out. At that point, the trajectory taken by my future mother, by the elfin-faced young woman in the photos from back then, by her body as it flew across the tarmac of a B-road, took a new and irreversible course, from which my own trajectory would subsequently emerge.

*

3

The second beginning of the story – even if, at the time, I had no idea that that was what it was – coincides with the autumn of the year I turned twenty-six, when I left the home and the city in which I had spent my entire life, and went to live in Milan. I lived in a studio flat on the third floor of a 1920s apartment block. It had a wooden floor and a white kitchenette in one corner and was flooded with light right through to evening – something I would later find oppressive, but not back then. It was the first place I ever had entirely to myself and I loved it as though it were human.

I spent my weekdays alone. I went out early every morning and wandered around the city going nowhere in particular. It was early September and, after a cool wet summer, a belated wave of heat surged through the still half-empty streets. Just around the corner from the road where I lived, in a street rather ethereally named after Fra Angelico, from one of the top-floor balconies one could, in the humming stillness, sometimes hear a canary sing, and from the bubbling rill of his song – that unmistakable song that sounds something like 'blublublublublu' and ends on a long flute-like top note – I still knew enough to tell that the bird was a Malinois waterslager (and for an instant the tender gloom of the aviary where, when I was a little girl, my uncle and I had checked the nests, spilled out across the pavement, together with the aviary's deep green smell). In that motionless air, the deserted buildings of the neighbouring science faculties gave the impression of having been abandoned many centuries ago. I walked for whole days at a time, down random streets, only very occasionally pulling out my phone to check where I was on the map. The city was entirely unfamiliar to me, and I to her, and this was, in its own way, comforting.

Sometimes an abrupt gust of wind roused the air, and patches of cloud-shade scudded across the façades, momentarily isolating a detail in a pool of light: a wrought-iron balcony; a roaring mouth crowning the mullion of a top-floor window. The colour of the façades shifted, quivered and then recomposed itself. I sat down to read on a bench in the shade. In the park at Porta Venezia a young woman was holding a cotton-bonneted baby to her chest, facing a tree. Its feet dangling, the baby examined the trunk with interest, his open palms pressed to the bark. The woman smiled almost imperceptibly, one eyebrow arched, as though she knew a secret. Whenever I happened to take the metro home after an evening out, my journey took me down a street where the grand arched windows of the Institute of Chemistry cast amber light into the gloom behind the dense, dark fronds of the elm trees. Once, in a back street behind Piazzale Loreto, I walked past a launderette where there were three young sailors who looked like they were Slavs. We stared at one another through the window with identical expressions of surprise, as though my presence there were every bit as improbable as their own. Russian sailors in a Milanese launderette! I shrugged – as convention dictates in such cases – and resumed my walk.

As had rarely been the case before then, entire days could go past without me speaking to anyone at all. Immersed in that prolonged and total speechlessness, the things I saw gained a strange clarity, like noises in the night which, amid the silence, always seem more distinct. But the images remained scattered and disconnected and apparently devoid of any significance apart from the passing interest they provoked as, one by one, they caught my eye. In that brief flicker of curiosity, some insignificant portion of my brain perhaps sensed that in some small way they originated within me; but that perception of a perception of a perception was so pallid, so slight, that it immediately dissolved, and the images were left floating against a hazy backdrop, growing increasingly anaemic. It didn't occur to me that there might be any link between me and those things, or to wonder what that connection might be.

Truth be told, everything seemed rather irrelevant to me. I had a bit of money because I had, indirectly, received a small inheritance which, together with my meagre and sporadic income, was enough to live on for a few months without a regular salary while waiting for the situation to improve. And it had to improve. It couldn't not. The financial crisis was an abstract entity, obscure and certainly irritating but not something that could *truly* affect my life in the long run. I just had to wait. So I waited. By profession I read French and English manuscripts for the foreign fiction department of a large publishing house. My job was to assess their suitability for the Italian market. It was a restful job, and by then I, too, felt tranquil.

The solitude was new to me – like a perfectly empty cathedral in which every stride produced an inordinate echo. You had to move with care and avoid paying too much attention to all those echoes, to the amplification of every muffled whisper. It was interesting, but tiring. At weekends, of course, my boyfriend N., who lived in a city nearby, used to join me. I had friends in the city, and met up with them regularly. But the huge sudden void that opened out on weekdays was hard. One lunchtime I began weeping for no particular reason while eating cherry tomatoes out of their plastic box. As the tears fell, I glanced at it distractedly and only then noticed that the label read 'Tomatoes For Aficionados'. God, what philistines, I thought, and the mental picture of me privately weeping as I ate tomatoes for aficionados was so silly that it calmed me down.

I wasn't writing. For years, by that point, I had been fixated with the same idea, which never amounted to more than a series of intentions, a vision of a series of sentiments. I knew what I wanted to talk about, but the how still escaped me. I just wanted the story to seem as detached from my own as possible. So I left the imagined novel – the shape of which seemed to be forever mutating – to roam, floating around my head with its exhaustingly fuzzy outline, a blue fog in which I occasionally ensnared a 'nice sentence' which sat there, isolated and useless. Sometimes the blonde spectre of M., my absent protagonist (who had already undergone several changes of identity, but whose primary narrative function was essentially to be dead) emerged from the mist, but I could never make out anything more than details: the downy golden hair on the back of her neck, her long feet, her slightly curved shoulders. I longed for her to become a coherent creature, but I never succeeded in pinning her down in her entirety. I had an unwavering and infantile faith in the fact that, sooner or later, it would happen. I just had to wait. In this case too, I just had to continue to think.

Approximately three weeks after I moved there, my mother came to visit. I showed her around the neighbourhood: we stopped in front of some words that someone had written on a wall near my house, under a white-framed window – 'OUT OF PLACE EVERY-WHERE' – and we pondered the irony of fate. It was a day that still felt summery, shimmering with light. Behind the gates of the apartment blocks' courtyards, the palms and eucalypti rustled, incongruous and enchanting, as though they had emerged from somebody's dream. My mother advanced like a slow, placid ship, benevolently observing the city and noting the details I pointed out. I remember absolutely nothing of what we said to each other that day, but that's immaterial: we continued a happy and unin-terrupted conversation which has been going on for ever.

At one point we entered a second-hand bookshop and I went down to the basement. She stayed on the ground floor to look at the shelf of books about the First World War (she had developed a mild obsession with the period since retiring, and she looked after the historical archive at the primary school she had taught at for the last eighteen years of her career). When I came back up and re-emerged from the metal staircase that surfaced in the middle of the shop, she turned to me, smiling and flushed, and then something happened, something very sudden that lasted precisely as long as it took me to put my foot on the topmost tread: for an instant, her face seemed distant and significant. As though I were already looking back at it. As though, for the length of that instant, the present, the past and a postulated future were superimposed. As though it were already a memory – one of those things to which we attribute no importance the moment they happen and which we look back on much later as a presage of something we will never truly understand: for an instant, my mother appeared to me in time. Then I reached the top of the staircase, she asked me, 'Have you found anything?' and that strange confusion ruptured – it would come back to me later that evening, when she had already left for home. But it remained inexplicable all the same.

Who was I? It was something I never asked myself. Firstly, like anyone who possesses a modicum of sanity, I was thoroughly sick of my own company. And secondly because I never felt the need. I thought of the years behind me as a sort of long single day, in the even white light of which my entire life up to that point seemed to have happened just hours earlier and to be perfectly plain to see. Because of my age, of course. After all, I hadn't actually been alive all that long. But also for another reason: ever since I had been capable of remembering, I had remembered a very great deal. And with very precise outlines. But more than that: confusedly but recognisably, I had the impression of there being a perfect continuity between the sense I had had of myself at eight, or twelve, or twenty, and how I felt now. Nearly everything I had ever seen happen or had felt, even many years earlier, even certain bizarre and unconfessable childhood emotions, was as clear and present as the yellow ceramic bowl in which I kept the fruit, as the cricket that had survived the end of the summer and continued its lonely chirruping near my window, or as the gurgling of the neighbours' newborn baby on the other side of the wall. I had no need to recall it. The past was a uniform expanse.

The young man runs through the night. He runs across the city, runs through the endless city. Tomorrow he will turn twenty-eight, and he is wearing pyjamas and he is shoeless and he is covered in blood not his own. It is the night before Christmas. The city sleeps on in the rain, unknowing and oblivious, its shutters lowered and its windows closed. It is, all of this, impossible.

'I think he got my aorta. I'm dying,' he had said. 'Get help.'

The young man runs.

The earlier masks have fallen; new masks will come. For now, time and the man are suspended. Everything he was, before tonight, disintegrating. He is stripped bare, frighteningly free, with a wild freedom, reckless and unrequested. He is frighteningly innocent. Blood, blood, blood. The only real *fact* shining into the night is the blood.

Perhaps his feet will be wounded, running like this, without shoes, without socks, on the asphalt. Running. His face tonight is invisible. His entire body a mechanical action pressing on towards where, towards what. How long the city lasts. The same streets as always, the streets of the living day, now unreal and unseeable and unfamiliar. Not one bar or restaurant is open: he has no idea what to do. He is innocent. He's scared. He knows nothing yet. He already knows it all. Forever.

The young man runs through the city of stone.

Two years before I moved to Milan, my father had died. It was 14 June 2011. So, at the moment of writing, just over six years ago. He had liver cancer, which had, in a matter of months, inevitably, statistically, reached his lungs. As he shrank and grew ashen, he told me he had an infection, in his lungs, a stupid infection that he'd picked up because he was still too weak from the illness he'd now got over. As he spoke, he used the technical jargon that was familiar to both of us for different reasons. I nodded, from the sofa in front of him. Did he know that I knew? Probably, yes. And anyway, he couldn't hide his terror. But by unspoken agreement we carried on like this right to the end.

When I had entered the room in the hospital he'd been taken to, with lung failure, two days earlier and where, an hour or so beforehand, his heart had finally given out, he was lying in his gown, his mouth open, as though he'd fallen asleep in an embarrassing position, and on his eyes there were two pads of gauze soaked in the liquid they use to keep the eyeballs detached. His wife explained – or perhaps she had already told me before I came in, I don't remember – that he had wanted, if nothing else, to donate his eyes – perhaps the only usable organs in a cadaver devastated by the disease. Inside the room there were other people, and they were crying in various corners. Then and there no one came over to greet me: apparently this wasn't my loss to grieve. I couldn't bring myself to look at the familiar body with the monstrous pieces of gauze on its eyes. I hovered around, keeping my back to the bed.

Outside, the air was oppressive. Muggy. The clouds were massing above the city in the gloom of an oncoming summer storm. It was my mother, coming back in from the hospital, having only just gone there, half an hour earlier, by bike, who had told me, astonished: 'He's dead.'

The eerie mugginess continued throughout the long senseless days of the wake, a full three days for some unexplained reason. And towards the end I watched with horror as my father's lips began to curl gently away from his teeth, decomposition beginning. He was small, almost sweet, beneath the extraordinary veil, with the crucifix that the funeral directors had placed on the coffin and which no one, it seemed, had disputed. A crucifix! On his face! Which, effectively, not even I had disputed. I was speechless, as though detached from this thing that was happening somewhere outside me. His long eyelashes, my long eyelashes, cast a shadow over his emaciated face. He wasn't unrecognisable. No, that wasn't the case at all. He didn't look waxen. He was himself, with no eyes beneath his lids now, but I wasn't disturbed by the idea. I sat there, on one of those plastic chairs they line up for these vigils, my head leaning back on the wall, and I continued to analyse it all relentlessly, the dirty light that fell from the window, the whispering at the door, the quality of the words I managed to catch, the generic squalor of the rooms where rituals of this kind take place, the repetitiveness of fate which had brought me back here so soon – first for a friend, now for my father; I analysed everything, but wearily. Almost in self-disgust. Almost as though I had no choice. And in reality I didn't, because *that was the way I was made.*

At the funeral, a secular service at the crematorium chapel of memory – that mawkish name they give to the place where bodies are burned – there were hundreds of people, but I recognised hardly any of them, apart from those who'd turned up for my sake. However, the number of people who came was the only remarkable thing about it. The whole event was pervaded with a terrible sense of impersonality. It could have been anyone's funeral. When I climbed on to the dais to read two poems (I had told myself I should; I had chosen two pieces, by poets I loved, for the simple reason that they were beautiful and had a liturgical ring to them and spoke of things that were somehow relevant in the most abstract and oblique way possible), I didn't know that I was looking out, amid the mass of faces, on to another unimaginable and secret trajectory. I didn't know that, but I wasn't looking for it: I was as blind as my newly dead and eyeless father.

I never once lifted my eyes while reading, my voice unwavering and resonant. Then I returned to my seat. I was twenty-four and wore my hair in a braid that wound around my head.

I didn't know much about him.

When we are young we confine ourselves to noting our parents' existence without being particularly interested in them. In addition to which, my father and I had lived in different houses for over twenty years, and for various periods of varying duration we had not spoken or had seen very little of each another. Ours was, as they say, a complicated relationship.

He was almost forty-two when I was born. He had always been baffling. I didn't really understand what job he did (when I was very little he had taught for a year or two at a private school, but after that, who knows?), or why he had started studying again. I scampered along behind him down the forlorn corridors of the university, and I read or played on my own while he held court among groups of students just out of their teens – his classmates. His beard was already silvery, although it conserved rusty streaks – a reddish watermark I share. In the greenish light of the Palazzo Nuovo building he seemed strange and sad, and out of place.

Back then he lived in an attic. The minuscule kitchen where we ate when I slept at his house had a big window looking out onto the rooftops. He had brought nothing with him. He seemed to have come from nowhere, as though nothing had ever happened before I existed. But for a five-year-old this is a perfectly acceptable sort of temporal reality: adults are a fact of life and an insoluble mystery; adults come and go, their faces appear and disappear, the rooms they live in have existed for ever and first come into being the moment you, the first human on earth, step through the door. Sometimes they are transient, sometimes they are as immutable as the mountains. You don't question their existence.

*

Of course he hadn't come from nowhere. He wasn't from Turin – and neither was my mother, who, at nineteen, like almost everyone she knew, had left her native village on the boundary between the province of Turin and the province of Cuneo. He came from the Gargano peninsula, but when he left school he moved to Rome to study medicine. (That was as much as I knew. How he then arrived in Turin, for example, no one had ever told me.) By then his accent was neutral, with no recognisable regional lilt. In the summer we sometimes went to visit his family for a day or two. He had two sisters and two brothers: he was the last but one. Three of them had stayed on in Puglia, although they all lived in different towns. The eldest, who had made his fortune, lived on Lake Garda and I hardly ever saw him. One or other of them would put us up when we visited. There was clearly something odd about their relationship and, equally clearly, my father was very different from his siblings. But these were things no one discussed. When he was down in Puglia he sometimes reacquired an accent of a sort, but for me, who knew how he normally spoke, it sounded affected, as though he were trying to go unnoticed. As though he were trying as hard as he could to resemble them.

**

When I was ten he graduated in psychology and from then on worked in residential care centres for drug addicts, the mentally ill and troubled teenagers. A few of the troubled teenagers came to the funeral, awkward and sweet, with their smart, ill-fitting suits and their long-wristed arms which they didn't know where to put, and their faces contorted in grief. So, this was what he had been doing in the last, let's say fifteen, years of his life. He had two other degrees, though: one, way back when, in medicine; another in jurisprudence. The connection between these things wasn't clear.

In any event, nothing in his appearance or his manner betrayed the fact that he was a cultured man. He was messy, noisy, carelessly dressed and had forever been as poor as a church mouse. For sixteen years, after the attic, he had lived with a woman he would end up deciding to marry a week to the day before he died. Or, to be more precise, he had gone to live *with* her, in the house she owned, and this had allowed him to enjoy a modicum of middle-class comfort. Amid her sober, elegant furniture, surrounded by her beautiful ceramics and the polished wood and the costly soaps, he was every bit as absurd as a penguin would be in the galleries of the Hermitage.

He was enthusiastic and sentimental (his postcards and messages, even when unashamedly practical, always had an elegiac flourish to them). He devoted himself with a defenceless fervour to all the things he cared about, such as his young drug addicts with their ashen faces and all his other assorted misfits, and he had a haphazard, almost boyish relationship with everything else – clothes, money, the future. Although he was capable of dreadful anger, outbursts of rage which, like a sudden wildfire, blackened everything in his wake, and although the words he used could be cruel (but all of this only with those closest to him), he was generally what one might call a cheerful man, lovable and candid by nature. He liked everyone, everyone had to be saved. Oh yes, his faith in others was boundless: in effect, he often met with burning disappointment. But he was also vain, and he revelled in the adoration of others, which he could inspire with surprising ease. And how it irked him that I, on the other hand, didn't worship him in the slightest. I found the contrast between his public and private personas very irritating (by private, I mean when it was just the two of us and we had no audience of any kind), as I did the fake, artificial mannerisms he adopted when anyone else was around; it was as though he were acting out an exaggerated version of the image he thought they had, or wanted them to have, of him. I watched him adjusting to the circumstances, slipping on different masks. There was the thoughtful intellectual, the lyrical nature lover, the matey simpleton and even, unfortunately, the inspired father, and all of them worked their inevitable magic: ecstatic admiration from his audience, incalculable annoyance in me. This had sullied everything. So by now, almost every time he expressed any form of emotion, I detected a note of falsity, an instinctive exhibitionism that probably wasn't, at the time, even there. But I was implacable. I never forgave him any of it.

He was quick to develop infatuations, but few of his friendships survived over time. Something that forms part of the natural course of human relationships (people drift apart from time to time, it's normal) in his life took on a form of pathological recursiveness. People he had been friends with for years, people with whom we had gone on holiday, vanished from one day to the next and were never spoken of again. The motives undoubtedly varied from case to case; the closure, though, was absolute. When, at fourteen, I had discovered quite by chance that, before getting together with my mother, he had once been married (what is more, to a woman whose home I had frequented throughout my childhood and whose new partner and children I knew), I had asked my mother, of all people, 'But why did he never tell me? What was the *point* of not telling me?' I was genuinely perplexed.

She had thought about it and then replied, 'He divides his life into compartments.' She could offer no other explanation. And in reality there were no other explanations, nor was there any real point in my father's omissions, in his tendency to dismantle the past. He moved from one scene in life to another in this fashion, hiding from those he'd previously been close to and offering himself unreservedly, swathed in a fictitious splendour, to those who next came along.

Even if he did all he could to ignore it, he had aged. Yet to me he gave the impression of being always the same, always predictable; an immovable man, wrapped up in the same old things, the same old poses, the same old words. I wasn't interested in deciphering him, nor did I think there was anything to decipher. He and his death were part of the terrain of obvious facts on which my life played out: the smooth, even surface over which I could pass an impassive hand and feel no residual ripples of any kind, despite the rage that rumbled beneath it like water under river ice in winter. Besides, what's interesting about an immovable man?

Strangely enough, he often appeared in my dreams. There was one which re-presented itself repeatedly and was almost identical every time, with minimal variations (and occasionally still does). He pretended to be dead, and in reality went into hiding for months and then for years. There was never any real reason for it. The coffin we'd gathered around had been empty; we had mourned a lie. He had lied to everyone, and above all he had lied to me.

'How could you do something like that?' I would ask him, with a neediness I found revolting. Or with a suffocating anger. Why had he put me through so much pain for nothing, and for so long?

More often than not his reaction was hostile, and, without turning to face me, he would answer coldly that it was something I wouldn't understand. On other occasions he was meek, silent and still unwell. He would shake his head very gently: he couldn't tell me. It was a mystery into which I would not be initiated.

There were also – but they were rarer – kinder dreams. In these we did the things we had always done together: we had coffee at a little table outside in the sun; we discussed innocuous frivolities. It was all very ordinary. But after a while a muffled sort of rumbling would reach me from what seemed to be a long way off and, astonished but relaxed, and in precisely the same tone as the rest of the conversation, I would ask him, 'But weren't you dead?'

(*Inter alia*, I know this happens to lots of people. Isn't it odd that this particular form of astonishment should be part of our collective repertoire of dreams? It's curious, isn't it, that almost all of us ask the same question of our dead nocturnal visitors. And then there's the version in which we know it, but they don't, and it seems rude to point it out. Buñuel, in his autobiography, describes a recurring dream in which his father would sit at the table with the rest of the family: 'I realise he's dead and whisper to my mother and sisters who are sitting next to me, "We mustn't under any circumstances let him know."')

Or, in yet another version, I would fail to notice anything amiss, and he remained alive, intact and normal, and continued to talk in his own voice, and walk by my side along the riverbank, with those short elastic strides of his, with the same old gait he'd always had.

The worst dream was one I had a year after he died, just before going off for an island holiday with one of my girlfriends. We were sitting at a table in an unfamiliar living room and he was still ill. Very ill. With a hesitant smile, I showed him a map of the island – an entirely imaginary version of the real one – and pointed to the places we would be going to; I told him that he, too, must have visited the same sites many years earlier. In a shrill, anguished voice, which now that I come to think of it reminds me of the avian shriek with which he had once, when he was already close to death, put the phone down on me in the middle of an argument, he had replied: 'I will never go anywhere again!'

If, while reading, I happened to come across an account of someone else's grief, or simply a description of a parent who sounded wonderful and had, quite evidently, been considered wonderful by the child who spoke of them, I felt a vague envy – in the same way that I have always envied fathers and children who love one another straightforwardly. I would read these things, moved and humbled, and it always seemed to me that their nostalgia was more respectable than mine. They had a *right* to suffer. Unlike them, I didn't feel I had any right to pine: we were not normal, our story was not a sweet one, the ghost I had been supplied with had none of the magic of Nabokov's father, forever enveloped in the summery light of a forgotten garden.

One day that first summer, during a lunch out in the countryside, Agata, my father's first wife, whom for years I had only ever seen at another family's parties, came up to me and said shyly that she had something to give me: it was a little black-and-white photograph which had been slipped inside a square envelope. A four- or five-year-old boy, at the seaside, standing on the seat in a beached rowing boat, proudly wearing a ridiculous ruched sun-suit, his hands on his hips, his little legs still chubby, his face wrinkled into a scowl because the sun was in his eyes. It must have been taken in 1949 or 1950.

'I wanted you to have it,' said Agata. I didn't dare look her in the eye, or find fitting words of gratitude or pleasure: I couldn't get any out. I understood the significance of the gesture she was making: for the very first time since my father had fallen ill, someone was acknowledging my filial prerogative and, in a certain sense, offering me a form of historical continuum. It was an extraordinary gift: she was saying, 'This belongs to you because you're his daughter', which in any other context might sound banal, but which burst its way into my story with the force of a dramatic revelation. But I didn't know how to communicate any of these things. And perhaps I didn't want to. I thanked her, took the photo home with me, put it away in a drawer, and only ever took it out to show it to a couple of friends, more in the manner of an item from a cabinet of curiosities than the potent talisman or the luminous and electrifying point of contact that it could have been. I had no other photographs of my father as a child, apart from one that was very ugly and battered and had already spent years buried beneath layers of other possessions. But beyond a conventional sort of tenderness, I didn't feel anything much. It wasn't a door onto anything. It was just an old photograph, sweet, funny and inert.

The summer I left home, my mother, a hoarder of some renown, had taken the epic decision to tidy up her room. Implausibly full cupboards and cabinets had been thrown open, large boxes overflowing with photos and documents had been emptied out, and the entire contents of her bookcases had left their shelves. The house had suddenly been invaded by a tsunami of dusty paper which occupied all the respirable air. My mother moved around amid the heaps overcome with a febrile excitement, with the shining eyes of a conqueror. She catalogued, she caressed, she commented, she sat on the floor rereading for whole days at a time, and she summoned me to act as an apathetic witness.

'Look at this! These were the books I used to buy at the newspaper kiosk when I was a girl!' she told me enthusiastically, waving scruffy copies of 1960s Oscar Mondadori paperbacks at me ('The "transistor portables" for your home library, presenting literature's masterpieces and all the most exciting stories, published weekly in unabridged *supereconomica* format to enjoy in your free time. Oscar paperbacks are 1965's books for the hardworking Italian. At home, on the tram, on the omnibus, on the trolleybus, on the underground, in your car, in a taxi cab, on the train, in a boat, in a motorboat, on a transatlantic ocean liner ...'), *Tortilla Flat*, *The Moon is Down*, *The Grapes of Wrath*, *Black Boy*, *The Razor's Edge*, etc. Almost all of their covers, in many cases inexplicably, featured young women whose eyes had no pupils, writhing in a dramatic brume of paint and succumbing to the Germans or the intensity of their emotions. The thirteen-year-old version of my mother, who visited the newsagents to buy *Intrepido* and other comics, had one day seen those covers appear in the racks like enticing promises of a greater, wider yonder. And, she told me, these had been her first 'real' books, bought with her own money once a week and read secretly in bed at night by the light of the streetlamp on the corner of the road, leaving the shutters just enough ajar that the stripe of light served its purpose without attracting adult attention. I couldn't help but grin: my own tactics had, of necessity, been much more baroque (I remember a scaffold of towels around the bedside lamp, isolating a sliver of light that needed to be invisible through the frosted-glass panes of my bedroom door, and not being able, in the dark, to find enough props and struts for it), and all because – I now discovered – she herself had significant expertise in the sector. Which perhaps explained why she had almost always caught me red-handed.

It was inevitable that, among the photos of children now adults and lost to time, their faces set for eternity in the faded smiles of far-off school trips, a red anorak occasionally still standing out brightly against the dulled colours of the rest like a slowly cooling star; among the Tsvetaevas, the Asimovs, the Shakespeares, the Lovecrafts, the Canettis, the Bakunins, the projects prepared for the Vallette district schools, the plaintive forty-year-old letters from her mother ('You do know we miss you, Margherita? You never come home, you never write to us, Margherita...' Margherita. Margherita ...), the blood test results, the discarded prints of famous paintings with their curling yellowed corners, the tax returns, the Uranias, the LeGuins, the Potoks, the Cedernas, the brochures, the exercise books full of lesson plans, the many photos of our life together, the essays on history and sociology; among the shells and fossils and stones which she gathered when out and about, when she went off on her long expeditions along the beach or up in the mountains and for hours on end her distant silhouette could been seen moving slowly and doggedly, her head bent to scan the ground for something worthwhile, for smooth igneous pebbles split open like wounds revealing grottoes of periwinkle-blue crystal, or a shiny piece of blackest-of-black obsidian with a tiny, enigmatic fleck of Persian blue, or a bulbous cluster of pyrite crystals; among the comics she had never outgrown – *Linus* and *Corto Maltese* and *Sturmtruppen* – printed on paper so cheap that they fell apart in your hands, and the letters from Costanza in America, the letters from school friends, the mounds of postcards that had traversed vast and heart-rending spans of time and space, the cards congratulating her on my birth, the paper bracelet which had encircled my newborn wrist in the hospital, the lonely buttons – from who knows which shirt and who knows which coat – that had ended up on the bottom of every drawer, the research papers on urban immigration, the Mancinellis, the Saul Bellows, the Akhmatovas, the Stajanos, the Arendts, the Bradburys, the exhibition catalogues, the honorary partisan's diploma that the Vallette section of the National Association of Italian Partisans had awarded her back when she was a head teacher, the Amos Ozes, the Queneaus, the Szymborskas, the Dolcis, the thrillers, the Ferreiro-and-Teberosky theory of learning, the poets, the poetasters, the pundits, the literary Leviathans, the seemingly infinite layers of her stuff … it was inevitable – as I was saying – that, sooner or later, something belonging to my father and his four-year sojourn there would turn up. (After all, with that total indifference of his to objects, he'd left something behind in every place he'd ever been in.)

One day, in fact, she appeared at the door of her room and said, 'I've found some of your father's papers. I think they regard his trial. Do you want to see them?'

I looked up from the book I was reading, not particularly interested. She was leaning against the doorframe, expectantly.

'No,' I said eventually, and went back to my reading.

'All right.'

She went back into her bedroom. The 'papers', to which neither of us paid any further thought, were stuffed into a box along with other assorted documents, and there they remained.

You who are well acquainted with writers' manuals, shrewd reader, will already have noticed the pistol hanging on the wall in the first act of our drama. I, on the other hand, a lackadaisical and passive figure (but also, very fittingly, somewhat delicate of constitution), drifted around Milan entirely unaware even of the possibility that, somewhere or other, a pistol existed.

Everything I did continued to have a light hue of unreality; I seemed to be forever playacting at something other people knew how to do properly, or for which they all had a natural talent. Life, I suppose. At the same time, I happily sank myself into the asinine minutiae of everyday practicalities. I even embraced the terror they induced in me: in any event, it was preferable to the terror I felt at the end of each day when I sat down alone at the kitchen table and didn't write. I couldn't even remember what it felt like. It was extraordinary to think that I had once known how (for all the clumsiness of my teenage experiments and what I now dismissively considered their blithe innocence), or that there had ever been any pleasure, excitement or passion there. But that was before the words ran aground on a nightmarish sandbank. Before Celina's cancer and death, and everything that had happened since.

It was all hypothetical now. And time went by. So much time had already gone by; and yet none of it went anywhere. It curled back in on itself.

Meanwhile, autumn came, and then winter, and there were so many things to think about and talk about and read, there were goings-on to be informed about and long solitary walks to be taken – I had such intense and bewildering feelings for my new city, for the fleeting visions of lobbies glimpsed from her open doorways, for her apartment blocks, for her trees, for the names of her streets, that there really wasn't much room in my life for anything else. There were deadlines to meet, there were moments of elation and moments of dejection, and nowhere, not even in the briefest of intervals, was there ever a thought for that forgotten, irrelevant episode back in the summer.

I went back to Turin for Christmas. The flat (which mentally, instinctively, I still called 'home': 'I'm going home') was the same as ever, the same old mismatched furniture, the riot of knick-knacks, the matchless amber gleam of its rooms. But something was different. I had already been back a couple of times since moving, and the distance between the two cities was hardly enough to have been disorienting, yet somehow I already felt that I no longer belonged there in quite the same way. Between me and those objects which were so familiar that they felt like extensions of my own body, time had interposed itself. Over the months, they and I had existed in parallel dimensions; they had, in a manner of speaking, led an independent life hidden from my view, and I couldn't not now see them through different eyes. I was discombobulated, but – as usual – didn't give it much thought.

What happened was this. On 26 December, partying done and friends gone home, my mother and I were alone in the house. It was a peaceful, drowsy evening and we chatted intermittently, with me sitting at the table, head propped on fist and eyes half-closed, she on the sofa, knotting that everlasting rug of hers (completing it would take her a further three years). We slipped into a conversation about my father. It was, in fact, his birthday. Or rather, it would have been. My mother asked, 'How old would he be?'

'He was born in 1945, so ... sixty-eight,' I calculated. It was a strange number to hear myself saying. There's always something funny about discussing the age of someone who no longer has one.

'In 1945? No, no. It was 1947.'

'Nope. You're getting him mixed up with your brother.'

But she insisted she was right, until in the end even I began to have doubts. Then she pointed a forefinger at nothing in particular and her face lit up.

'You know where we can check? Do you remember those papers of his, the ones we found when I was tidying up?'

'Uh-huh.'

'The one on the top of the pile had his date of birth on it. Just give me a second ...'

I followed her into her bedroom and sat on the bed while she looked for it. She opened up the big box it was in, pulled out a sheaf of papers that had been stapled together, and scanned the first page. Then she looked back over her shoulder.

'Nineteen forty-five. You were right.'

'Told you.'

'This must be the verdict of acquittal,' she added a beat or two later, her eyes glued to the document once more.

This time round I forced a flicker of interest out of myself. I stuck out a hand.

'Give us a look.'

She was wrong (I think she'd never actually read it before): it wasn't the verdict of acquittal, but the notice and grounds of appeal that my father's lawyer had lodged at the Court of Cassation before the third hearing. That was plain from the preamble: 'In the Court of Cassation, In the matter of an application for leave to appeal against conviction, Notice and Grounds of Appeal to the Court of Cassation by Dr LEONARDO BARONE, born at Monte Sant'Angelo on 26 December 1945 and currently residing at Via V..., Turin, represented in this matter by counsel M.S., against the ruling made on 19 June 1986 (no.11/86) by the Second Court of Assizes of Appeal of Turin, which by resorting to a *reformatio in peius* amended the sentence imposed by the Court of First Instance and condemned the appellant to ... years of imprisonment for the crime of participation in an armed band.'

Participation in an armed band. Now this, suddenly, was interesting.

I already knew – albeit very roughly – what had happened, but the title of the offence, typewritten on that now-yellowed sheet of paper, and the preposterousness of seeing those words associated with that familiar name, had a whole new and violent effect. As if only in that instant had the thing become real, ripped away from the hazy, colourless, ill-defined landscape of other people's pasts, of the lives lived by others when we weren't present.

I can't remember when it was that I first found out my father had been in prison. I couldn't say who it was that told me, or what the circumstances were, or how old I was, but I must have still been fairly tiny. I do remember the sensation, though: the menacing, fairy-tale equivocalness of the word (it may well be that they used the word *jail*, and that my memory of it had mutated), and the confused sense of it being something strident: a piece of information of that kind had no obvious place in the world as I knew it. But it had been a long time ago, they told me, and anyway he was innocent. Of that, I was never in any doubt. I had no idea what they could possibly have accused him of, but it was blindingly obvious that he couldn't be guilty; I might have had a little difficulty in actually defining his virtues, but he definitely didn't show any signs of a bent for crime. And that was as far as it went – a rush of childish compassion for him, whom I knew to be weak and therefore, axiomatically, a victim. Even as I grew older it was never a question to which I attached any importance; when I thought about him, it never occurred to me. We had talked about it a couple of times, but only ever cursorily. He had told me that he had been a doctor; that he'd been arrested and accused of being a terrorist; that the other doctors at the hospital he worked at had turned their backs on him, and for that reason he hadn't wanted to go back there and had abandoned the profession; that in the end he had been acquitted on all counts (I'd been born and was already a year old by then); that he had never been a terrorist. And on that count, I continued to have no difficulty in believing him. And that was that – apart from the odd comment made over the years. On one occasion: 'Someone from Front Line was wounded, and I treated them, *ergo*,' with a sarcastic emphasis on the illogical connection, 'they accused me of being a member of Front Line.' Were those his precise words? Yes, I think they were, more or less. (I do remember the sarcasm, because it was so out of character.) I don't think he ever furnished any other details. And I never asked.

On one of the rare occasions on which the topic was broached, I had said something like, 'One day you'll have to tell me the whole story.' He had smiled uncomfortably and had replied that it was all rather complicated, but yes, he would do. He never did.

As I began to leaf through the defence statement, that was, therefore, as much as I knew: next to nothing. I thumbed the edge of it. There were sixteen typewritten, numbered pages. It was a photocopy of the original.

The court of first instance found the appellant guilty of membership of the armed band known as Front Line, ruling that (p.184), 'independently of his critical stance with regard to Front Line's political aims, and despite having no formal role within the organisation, the said Dr Barone knowingly contributed to the activities of the group via his efforts to offer medical assistance to one of their militants (Galiani) and by travelling to Rome with the intention of offering medical assistance to another militant (Mancini) whom he failed to meet for reasons beyond his control, and by offering to make himself available to provide medical assistance to militants who might be wounded in the course of the organisation's future activities, and he thus contributed to the constitution and advancement, or reinforced the organisational structure of the group, of which he was therefore a de facto member.'

The *said* Dr Barone. Who was this unfamiliar figure, this stranger emerging from the mists of legalese, preceded by a very lawyerly prenominal adjective?

His lawyer continued: Dr Barone's original legal representative had lodged grounds of appeal running to twenty-eight pages, challenging in detail the trial judge's assessment of the probative value of the three items of evidence which purported to show that Barone was a member of Front Line,

namely: 1) the fact that during the month of March, 1979, he, a physician, examined and treated a wounded militant by the name of Mure Galiani; 2) the fact that during the month of January, 1982, he travelled to or promised to travel to Rome for the purpose of offering medical assistance to a second militant, Mancini; 3) the fact that he subsequently agreed to make himself available to provide further medical assistance should other militants be wounded in the course of future operations.

The Court of Appeal had discounted those twenty-eight pages, ruling that the evidence was fully sufficient to show that the defendant 'had indeed participated in a criminal association', above all in light of the statements made by various witnesses (i.e. repentant terrorists), thus confirming the ruling of the court of first instance.

In addition to which the second ruling noted simply:

> the evident weakness a) of Dr Barone's argument that 'he was undoubtedly and by his own admission well-known in subversive circles but had never been directly involved in them, and could not therefore be said to have participated in the armed band', b) of Dr Barone's reasoning with regard to 'his wholesale disapproval of all forms of violence, while entirely contradicting this by frequenting subversive milieus'.

It is hard to explain just how astonishing these words were, how unreal they seemed, there on my mother's bed between the tall, dark bookcases, there beneath the framed photo of an Alice-band-wearing eight-year-old me on the riverside in Rotterdam, there at the heart of that comforting archipelago of forever-familiar objects. The contrast was so extreme that I felt no nameable emotion, just a sort of vague detachment. They were words from an alien universe, they were words that belonged in a late-night documentary with a sombre soundtrack over the closing credits, or in the footnotes of one of the political history essays I used to devour; they didn't belong in my life, and above all – above all – it was inconceivable that they should be connected with the man I had known, that meek sixty-year-old man who, as I had turned up to meet him one day and had caught sight of him from a long way off, clinging to his bicycle, his cap – as it inevitably was – askew, a blank stare on his face, had seemed so utterly defenceless and fragile that I felt a rush of inexplicable anguish and quickened my pace until I almost broke into a run, in order to get to him as fast as I could and protect him from the cruelty of the world and enfold him in my orbit.

I had to stand up and walk around the room. Then I sat back down and continued reading.

As I pushed my way through the curtains of legal jargon, I

began to understand that the lawyer had believed the appellate court's ruling to be invalid because unjustified, in that the court had 'failed to consider the grounds of appeal', and had failed to evaluate relevant evidence. In other words, there were elements that had been disregarded by the first judge and which the second judge had 'entirely discounted' when reiterating the reasoning set forth in the initial ruling, while technically the appeal court should have considered, 'fresh evidence, apparently credible, such that, if given, could reasonably be expected to affect the result of the appeal'. The lawyer then analysed the alleged proof of guilt. Some sections had been underlined by my father, with funny stubby arrows drawn next to the salient points (I know the underlining was his because there was also a note scribbled in the margin in his illegible scrawl).

The first factum probans was inferred from statements made by members of Front Line who reported asking Dr Barone to provide medical assistance to Galiani, who had been wounded while engaged in operations on behalf of the band.

[...]

a) Barone, at the time of the request, was extraneous to Front Line and the decision to apply to him for help was made solely in light of the urgent necessity of the medical intervention (Celauro, interviewed by the Examining Magistrate, 7.10.1982: 'Barone definitely wasn't involved in Front Line. We decided to ask him for help anyway.'; Bo, interv. by Exam. Magistr., 11.10.1982: 'Barone wasn't a member of Front Line, but a decision was made to approach him in order to find out if he would be prepared to treat the injured comrade.');

b) at the time of the request, Barone had not been made aware that the injured man was a member of an armed band nor that he had been wounded while engaged in committing a criminal offence (Celauro, interv. *supra*: 'Meli said a comrade was wounded, but didn't go into any detail.');

c) a full month after unsuccessfully treating Galiani's wounds, Dr Barone was still considered external to the organisation, as evidenced by the fact that he was kept in the dark with regard to the circumstances in which the man had been injured (Bo, interv. *supra*: 'Verderame gave Barone a look that told him it was a subject best not discussed, and it went no further.')

The grounds of appeal argued that the court should consider the possibility that these statements 'confirmed the supposition that Dr Barone had agreed to offer medical assistance to Galiani for purely humanitarian motives and without knowing that the man was a member of an armed band, ergo the impossibility of inferring from the interview evidence that Barone had knowingly contributed to the activities of the organisation'. Nothing doing.

Then another figure of whom I'd never heard was introduced.

The second factum probans was inferred from statements made by the 'State's witness' Colomba to the effect that, at approximately 11 a.m. on the 23rd day of January 1982 [*what glorious, dementedly novelistic precision of detail!*] (so, a full three years after the Galiani episode), Barone made an undertaking to Colomba and to other members of Front Line who had asked him to take the 13:30 train to Rome in order to reach a woman by the name of Mancini who had been injured in the course of an operation organised by the band. It has been ascertained that Dr Barone did not take that train and that at 3 p.m. on the day in question he sent a certain Longo to Colomba, arranging for them to meet one another at 6 p.m. that evening; having organised the meeting, he then informed Colomba that he did not intend to make the journey to Rome.

Barone has always maintained: that at 11 a.m. he had made only a provisional undertaking, being torn between a humanitarian instinct to help someone in need of medical assistance and his disapproval of Front Line's aims and methods; that by 3 p.m. he had already decided not to leave for Rome, because his disapproval had won out; and that at 6 p.m. he had informed Colomba both of his decision not to travel and of the political motivations for it.

But this meticulous inventory of the inner peregrinations of our new and unfortunate Leopold Bloom (same initials, sadder fate) over the course of that long and momentous day had been neatly reinterpreted by the judges:

> The ruling of the court of first instance noted that at 7 p.m. on the day in question, in a conversation with an accomplice by the name of Nardelli, Colomba had made no mention of Barone refusing to leave for Rome, but in reference to the matter had asserted that at 6 p.m. Barone had simply informed Colomba of his intention to postpone his departure until such time as the ongoing police checks were relaxed.

The defence remarked that this would have been an infantile excuse, given that the police checks, which were being run that day in the wake of the killing of two carabinieri near Monteroni d'Arbia, would clearly not have eased off in such a short space of time. Moreover, Colomba himself had changed his version of events as soon as my father was arrested, declaring that it wasn't true and that Barone played no part in what, with a twisted euphemism, they referred to as 'the organisation'. (To say nothing of all their other words: their 'programmes' and 'methods'. Methods ...)

> Dr Barone's grounds of appeal stressed that Colomba had told the Court that at 11 a.m. Barone had given his consent with very little conviction (Colomba, interv. by Exam. Magistr., 31.7.1982: 'His "yes" wasn't a confident one; he wasn't happy ... I remember Leonardo strongly criticising the killing of the two carabinieri near Siena'), and that at 6 p.m. he had justified his refusal on political grounds (Colomba, interv. *supra*: 'There's something I want to add. There's a detail I've just remembered, and I'm 100 per cent sure about this. In Corso Peschiera, when Leonardo told me he wouldn't be going to Rome [...] he said that Front Line was just ridiculous, in the sense that the group's methods were unacceptable').

On the basis of these phrases, the grounds of appeal suggested that when, at 7 p.m., Colomba had spoken to Nardelli, who was in a certain sense the instigator, he had deliberately kept quiet about Barone's refusal; this because – according to the lawyer – Colomba was 'psychologically fragile' and wanted to avoid annoying Nardelli of whom he was profoundly in awe. The monstrous stupidity of it all was hardly lost on me, but I found other things in this passage more immediately striking – things less easily defined: the reference to a location very real to me – the long straight line of Corso Peschiera with its tall twin rows of hackberry trees (I'd driven down it hundreds of times, sitting in the car with someone or other); the vivid presence of my father moving and speaking in that city which all of a sudden seemed unfamiliar and crepuscular; the informal 'Leonardo', which, among other things, suggested that this Colomba figure must have been a friend of sorts.

The third item of evidence adduced against Barone, consisting of his promise to make himself available to offer medical assistance to militants who might be injured in the course of future operations, was inferred from statements made by the co-defendant Garbarino, who at that time went by the *nom de guerre* Asa.

The grounds of appeal point to the fact that Garbarino (Asa) had admitted to never having spoken directly to Barone, but had requested his availability via Colomba, who acted as a go-between and who a) in an interview with the Exam. Magistr. on 27.7.82 declared: 'Asa told me to telephone, but I only pretended to make the phone call. I told Asa I'd gone to make the call because he was very angry that day and I didn't want to upset him. But I didn't really call Barone that day'; b) in an interview with the Exam. Magistr. on 31.7.82 he added: 'I'm sure Asa only asked me to speak to the doctor that one time … it didn't happen again. I'm certain of that.

And so the grounds of appeal objected that all of this had been illegitimately accepted as evidence against the accused on the basis of mere hearsay, 'while the only person who would have spoken directly to Barone (in other words, Colomba) denied he had done so'. They established, therefore, that Barone had only declared his availability on a single occasion: and that was of undeniable relevance, given that, when he offered medical assistance to Galiani, the appellant had merely treated a wounded man, without knowing that the latter was a member of Front Line; while in the case of the second episode (involving the journey not made to Rome), he had initially agreed without much conviction, and had changed his mind over the course of the afternoon. Added to which, if he had only been asked on a single occasion to make himself available to offer future medical assistance, he could hardly be considered to have knowingly participated in Front Line.

Essentially, the charges laid against him only partially corresponded with the version he had sketched out for me. There had been much more going on. But the gaps still remaining were too important to allow me to form a clear picture. Why was he, by his own admission, 'well-known in subversive circles'? How was that possible? In what setting and in what circumstances could someone – a person who belonged to an armed band – have ended up looking at him in a way that would tell him, 'it was a subject best not discussed'? And what subject? At the end of the day, from his lawyer's point of view this was simply a recap of known facts which repetition had drained of impact, a careful gleaning of any statements made to the court that might help him make his desired point. From my point of view, it was as frustrating as seeing someone in the distance waving a placard with something written on it, and knowing that it was important but not being able to make it out, and then that someone vanishing promptly into the darkness.

There was one more passage that caught my eye, a few pages on.

Throughout the trial, Barone has repeatedly admitted having always 'been involved in politics' in Turin within the context of the so-called extreme-left or autonomist circles from which, at a certain point, the armed subversive movements evolved; the fact that he frequented such circles and was well-known within them is perfectly compatible, both logically and in terms of historical experience, with a rejection of violence and with a refusal to endorse or participate in organisations which employ that violence. Barone's accusants have themselves acknowledged that this was indeed his political stance. Colomba, interviewed by the Exam. Magistr. on 27.7.1982, declared: 'While we were chatting, I asked Barone, in a jokey way, if he wanted to join the organisation. He started laughing and didn't even answer the question ... I want to be clear about this: as far as I can see, Leonardo could never have been a Front Liner.' And Garbarino, interviewed by the Exam. Magistr. on 30.7.1982, said: 'I've heard Leonardo Barone speaking in public on a few occasions and his frames of discourse certainly weren't consistent with those of our organisation.'

Well yes, I thought, half smiling. Of course he 'could never have been a Front Liner'. Up to that point and in all its simplicity, it was the most accurate definition of my father I'd yet read, and finally corresponded with something I recognised (or had deduced): his nature.

But the judges were of a different opinion. And so, the appeal ruling had also denied 'that the appellant's minimal contribution to the commission of the offence justified a reduction in sentence, noting that the crime of participation in an armed band, ex art. 306 co. 2° c.p. is, by its very nature, a strict liability offence for which the exemptions provided for by art. 114 co. 1° c.p. cannot be invoked', etc., etc..

And then there were a few other things, and then, 'for the above and foregoing reasons, and in light of such further or other evidence as may be adduced', counsel requested that the Most Excellent Supreme Court quash the appellant's conviction. *Con ossequio*. Respectfully.

The pistol had blown up in my face.

I wouldn't have been able to tell you precisely what it was that had happened, but in the days that followed I was continually aware of something changing, imperceptibly but decisively; it regarded the way I looked at the city, certain things I now remembered: snatches of conversation, long-forgotten facial expressions, a tone of voice. Even Piazza Vittorio, the vast square next to which I had lived my entire life and of which I knew every inch, that white, hard-edged, perfectly geometrical piazza gaping open towards the bridge and the river and the hills, seemed to me – when I walked down there the following day and looked at it, empty of people and almost transparent in the glassy winter light – to be lunar and remote, as though signalling something mysterious. I remembered that one of the attics behind those dark dormer windows had been a Red Brigade hideout, or something of the sort, and I went off to find out. And in fact (I rediscovered, reading about it), at number 21, Patrizio P., the Red Brigade column leader, the first of the supergrasses, had lived in hiding and had been arrested, there in the street outside. And number 21 was right on the corner of my street. And for the first time in my life this shocked me. It suggested, in the same way that certain details in the notice of appeal had suggested it, a startling proximity in time and space which had never occurred to me before. Because, although my early childhood seemed to have taken place in a world that already belonged to a different century, I now realised (those dates in ink on paper had made me realise) that the interval was negligible: I was born only five years after my father's arrest. In fact, I already existed at a time when this thing was still unfolding.

My parents were left wing, like everyone they mixed with. It was normal. It was the standard backdrop to my childhood. So it was no great surprise that he'd been a militant, and not much of a surprise that this had involved the 'so-called extreme-left'; what I hadn't expected to discover was that he had, by all accounts, been a fairly well-known figure. From the quiet, colourless life he'd led afterwards, I would never have guessed. Why had he never talked about it? Why had he shied away from his own story? Who was my father?

Who would ever have imagined that was a question I would end up asking?

I had a confused sensation that in this thing – this secret – there must be something that had always escaped me, something fundamental. It was a nebulous sensation that accompanied me everywhere, like a hidden treasure sewn into the lining of a coat.

My mother didn't know much more than I did: when she first met him, he had never wanted to talk about what had gone on. It was as though he'd taken refuge in her house. And he preferred to hear her talk about herself, about books and about what she was doing at school, which seemed to him to be the last true political battlefront possible; if ever he talked about politics it was usually in general terms, without going into any details about what he had done personally. Their worlds were so different and so separate that my mother had never come into contact with his, apart from one very brief occasion, at a political meeting in 1980 in Vallette, five years before she met him. She had sensed that she represented a form of shelter, from the past as much as anything, and while she knew about his time in prison – he was, after all, obliged to report to police headquarters once a week; he wasn't allowed to leave Italy and always talked about how he wished he could go to Paris; and once, when they were on holiday in the Aeolian Islands with a group of friends, he forgot (or perhaps it was a tiny, silent rebellion) and the carabinieri came to look for him up on the cliffs; and this business of having to report in was sometimes spoken of as an irritant and worse, as something insufferably unjust – and while she knew he had been a militant, she had understood that it was something he wanted to bolt shut and walk away from. That he *needed* to.

There were, however, still a few people we knew who had, to one degree or another, been part of that former life and who would perhaps be able to tell me something about it.

So I made a couple of phone calls. 'There's this thing I've found. I'll try to explain,' I said hurriedly. 'One of these days, if you don't mind, I'd like you to tell me about my father's trial and everything that happened. And about who he was.'

On the other end there was a moment of astonished silence. They'd certainly never expected to hear me ask that. But then they said yes.

I had no real idea what I'd learn; I hoped that by putting together their fragments, the different things each of them knew or thought they knew, I would better understand what the story was. I wanted to fill in the gaps in the defence statement. I wanted the bare facts.

'Ah!' said my mother with a little laugh, when I told her what I was planning. 'The facts. They won't ever be the *facts*; you do know that, don't you?'

'Of course I do. Don't forget I studied comparative literature.'

'And you do know there'll be at least a hundred different versions of your father, whoever it is you end up speaking to.'

Yes, I knew that. While that's pretty much true of any human being, his was undoubtedly one of the more remarkable cases. I'd never met anyone who managed to inspire such passionate love, antipathy and disappointment, no one who had been eyed in such radically different ways. But there had to be some faint general outline, some clue to follow, that shadow of his – not a mask: something *real* – something I had seen flickering across the pages of the notice of appeal.

In the warmth of the kitchen, while we said these things to one another, there was a strange sort of pleasure in the air, a shared contentment. I can see my mother now, sitting at the other end of the table with a coffee cup in front of her, those slightly almond eyes of hers narrowed into a smile. She approved.

*

Before leaving for Milan, I dug out Agata's number and phoned her, too. She was astonished when she realised it was me; we'd never spoken on the phone before and we hadn't seen one another for a very, very long time. When I explained what it was about, she was disconcerted, almost offended. She was, it dawned on me, still offended at the idea of associating my father with the trial.

'But that had nothing to do with what he was. Nothing,' she said. '*That* wasn't him. Why do you want to know about that? What purpose would it serve, now?'

I couldn't think how to reply. It felt indelicate to say that it was just that I was interested. Which would, in any case, have been only half an answer.

She went on, and there was a certain urgency to her tone: 'You have no idea. You have no idea what those years were like. They've completely erased us. All anyone remembers is the murderers. You have no idea how much *happiness* was on offer. And we were happy.'

I said nothing, again.

'All anyone remembers is the murderers,' she repeated. She was silent for a bit, and then added, 'You do know your father wouldn't want you to write about this? You know they asked him to? Other people did ... his lawyer. They begged him to because he was "representative". But he didn't want to. He didn't want to remember it.'

In effect, I did know that. It was one of the few things my father had told me. He'd said they had wanted him to write a memoir, but he had refused. He hadn't offered any further explanations; although I remembered him closing his eyes for a second, as though he were disgusted or pained. But I had no intention of writing about it: the need I felt was different, it was recondite – and therefore incommunicable, especially to Agata, who was effectively a stranger to me: I simply wanted to know a bit more. At the very most, I thought, I might write a short piece based on the notice of appeal, using the details they were all going to give me. I already had an idea of how it could be done, if they gave me enough material. The title – with commendable originality – would be 'The Trial'.

Impatiently and, at the end of the day, quite sincerely, I said, 'I don't want to write about it.'

She sighed. I'd convinced her. We would meet up.

Over the following weeks I did some research. Mure Galiani, for example, which was a name I hadn't known, or perhaps didn't remember. With a vague sense of unease, I read that he had been injured during an assault in which an eighteen-year-old lad had, by mistake, been killed. Galiani's wounds were initially medicated in Turin, and then the 'comrades' had taken him back to Milan, where he was operated on in secret. I checked: it was the right month. March 1979. That was when my father had been asked to offer him medical assistance, according to the grounds of appeal, so this was the same episode. Was it possible that, at the moment in which he walked into the flat (I imagined it being a flat) where a guy with machine-gun wounds was waiting for him, presumably several hours after the shoot-out, he still hadn't known anything about it, hadn't connected the two things: the wounded man there in the flat, and the dead lad lying on a pavement a few miles away, in Borgo San Paolo? All things considered, if he hadn't listened to the radio and if whoever it was that took him there hadn't offered any explanations – which was more than likely – it wouldn't be so strange. What questions had he asked himself, as he bent over that man? What went through his mind? Why had it been him they called?

The grounds of appeal focused almost entirely on the second episode, the farce of three years later. This first episode had barely been mentioned: there wasn't even a note of the precise date. The lack of information was infuriating.

I couldn't find Colomba's name anywhere.

I decided to write to an old schoolmate who was a couple of years younger than me and whom I hadn't seen since we'd left school. At the time I hadn't known it – they'd told me later – but his father had been my father's lawyer, and had dealt with the first two stages of the court case (he wasn't the author of the notice of appeal, who had only handled the third stage).

It was he (the lawyer) who called me. One evening in early January. My hand began trembling when he told me who he was, but he seemed agitated too. His voice was soft, almost emotional. As though he were pleased I'd decided to look him out.

'I was very fond of your father, you know,' he said in conclusion. 'Come and see me whenever you want. I'll tell you everything I can.'

And so, towards the end of January, I found myself in the lawyer's office, in Turin. A tactful secretary led me into a room and asked me to wait there for a few minutes. I went over to the window. The day was bright and clear and the tree-lined avenue, with its naked horse chestnuts, seemed gilded. It glittered. Looking out on it, I was curiously calm, almost happy – a quiet, conscious happiness. I knew that this was a significant and irreversible moment. I knew I was about to set in motion something that would mark a dividing line between a before and an after in my life. I knew all of this, as I stood at the window with my hands resting on the sill.

A few days earlier I had spoken to Agata again, to arrange our meeting. She had asked for a copy of the notice of appeal, because she had never read it. When, in passing, I had mentioned Colomba's name, her voice had cracked in anger.

'It was Colomba who betrayed your father,' she spat out slowly. 'He was a friend of his. They were colleagues, at the factory, and your father had helped him out because he had a little boy who was ill. Colomba was one of those insignificant foot soldiers the armed parties had, the guys who handed out pamphlets on the factory floor, that sort of thing. When they took him in, they asked him for names in return for a reduced sentence, because that's what they did, and he didn't have any names to give them, they'd all been arrested by then, almost all of them, it was all over, and so he gave them your father's. Colomba knew full well he didn't have anything to do with Front Line. He knew that. He named him anyway, then he took it all back when he realised what he'd done, but by then it was too late. He ruined your father's life.'

I had remained silent for a moment, while the pieces in my head rearranged themselves, yet again, into another unexpected picture. So, that was what had happened. That's who Colomba was. That was why.

Putting the phone down, I felt a violent wave of nausea and a violent urge to let it all drop. For the first time, I was beginning to see that beneath the rock I was lifting up there lay a ferment of broiling darkness much vaster than I was maybe willing to brave. I sat down on the sofa with my head in my hands. I was too lazy and too gutless for all of this, and I knew it. When the going got tough, I normally wandered off somewhere with a book. But the truth was, the other, competing urge was infinitely more powerful. And infinitely more intense.

I had wondered if I should look for Colomba and ask him for his version. His 'version of events'. The staleness of the cliché irritated me. I had vetoed the phrase and the hypothesis, and brushed Colomba aside, for the time being at least. (And then, what sense would it have had? I asked myself. Turning up at his door like a vengeful ghost from the past, to remind him of something shameful, something he would certainly have no desire to recollect; provoking a pointless anguish, and all for what? Out of a love of completeness? And then, it wasn't as though the idea of laying eyes on him exactly thrilled me.)

So, there I was, looking out of the window, waiting for it all to begin.

The lawyer came into the room and said, 'Marta,' and walked over to shake my hand, with an affectionate smile. He asked me to sit down. He sat down on the other side of the heavy walnut desk and leaned forward.

He was sixtyish, with grey hair and a side parting, a curl grazing his forehead; a broad, good-natured face with a light veil of beard, and very blue, kind eyes somewhat at odds with his thick, still-black, Mephistophelian eyebrows.

He knew why I was there and what I wanted, and so, without too much preamble, he began talking. He told me he'd met my father at some political meeting or other at university, and that although they lived very dissimilar lives and he was much younger, they had become good friends, and he often saw my

41

father at protests or bumped into him when they were out and about; it wasn't an intimate friendship, but it was certainly the kind of friendship that meant that, when my father was arrested, he hadn't thought twice about taking up his defence. Over the years in which the hearings took place they had become much closer, and then – as often happens in life, he said with a soft, sad smile – they had lost touch.

He had looked around for any documents that might have survived the trial, but they were all lost in the meanders of the Court of Justice, and he doubted he'd manage to find anything. He would continue looking.

'There's a scene I remember from the trial,' he said. 'Leonardo was saying that there was an abyss between him and Front Line. I remember that being the word he used, and I remember the emphasis he put on it. And the procurator interrupted him with a derisive laugh, saying, "An abyss, no less!" And Leonardo was furious but also glacial, and he looked at him and said, "Yes. An abyss."' He remained silent for a moment, his thoughts far away. Then he said that it had all been complicated by the fact that some of my father's friends, trying to be helpful, had made false statements about his movements, contradicting his own statements and worsening his situation. In short, their intentions had been good, but the result was awful.

He didn't remember how many months my father had spent in jail. Less than a year, at any rate. He said that being there seemingly hadn't changed him in any way, he'd remained the same person he'd always been: he cooked, he organised protests against the conditions the inmates were held in, he had started studying law, right there in jail, so that he would be better equipped to defend himself (and perhaps also, I thought, to fill the vast and terrible emptiness of his time in prison). He was the same old Leonardo, remarked the lawyer. When I told my mother this, she paused for a while; then she said quietly, 'But at night? What must the nights have been like?'

I asked him about Colomba.

'Oh, Colomba ... Colomba was just a harmless little fellow,

seriously. He was a simple soul, semi-illiterate, and got dragged into something too big for him. Leonardo used to say the same thing ... he didn't hold it against him.'

'Do you think there'd be any point in trying to contact him?'

'Well, from what I've heard, he may even be dead. A couple of years ago, I think. I couldn't swear to it, though.'

Dead! The possibility had never even crossed my mind. Whichever way I turned, there seemed to be a new crevasse opening up at my feet.

'You know where we might find something, though?' said the lawyer. 'There's the Bianca Guidetti Serra archive at the Piero Gobetti Study Centre. There might be something there, even if she wasn't involved in your father's case. They have lots of files on the Front Line trials. I'll come with you, tomorrow. We can look together.'

The following day was grey and cold; we met up in Piazza Arbarello – another familiar location which had suddenly acquired a new significance (and would soon acquire yet another one: little by little the city was redoubling itself). The building in which the archive was housed looked just like so many others in Turin, with its ageing antique-yellow paint which had begun to flake, and a big dark door, and wrought-iron grates at the windows. There was a plaque, which I stopped to read; it began: 'In this house Piero Gobetti spent the final years of his short life, and from here he set off to face exile and to meet his death.' The words 'short life' moved me: they were sweeter and more human than the bombast conventionally reserved for commemorative plaques.

'In we go!' said the lawyer.

The archive was on the first floor: dark rooms and corridors overflowing with dusty files which reached all the way up to the ceilings. There were over six hundred of them. Fifty years of work. Bianca Guidetti Serra's entire life as an activist lawyer – Guidetti Serra who, only a few months later, would die at the age of ninety-five. (I remember meeting her once, with my mother, in Via Pietro Micca: a diaphanous little old lady leaning on a walking stick, her white hair glowing in the sun. My mother had whispered, 'That's Bianca Guidetti Serra,' and both of us had held our breath in a devout silence, as though it were the whole of the twentieth century walking past us, or the city's tutelary spirit.)

A young lawyer who looked after the archive was waiting for us: it would be a complicated piece of research, he told us, because the archive still needed to be reorganised, the innumerable documents it contained hadn't yet been catalogued. There were other problems, too: as my father's heir, I could only consult files which regarded him directly, not other people; even if those other people's files contained material that regarded him. Forty years would have to have gone by, he said, for the material to be available to the general public. In our case, only thirty-two years had gone by: I would clearly have to resign myself.

We poked around for hours, the lawyer, the young archivist and I, and we found one generic file which regarded the Front Line trials from 1981 and 1982. I sat down at a big table in a half-lit room and began to read. The lawyer had another appointment to get to and had to rush off; I was left alone with the young man, who wandered in and out and, intrigued by my story, asked me a question every now and then. I did, in effect, find a few pages about my father in the file – but just an outline report of some kind which didn't add much to what I'd already read. In addition to that, all I found was a single comment noting the 'insolent' attitude he displayed when insisting that he had nothing to do with the armed band; and also noting that, on the day in which Mure Galiani was wounded, it couldn't have been a mere coincidence that the Front Liner sent to find a doctor had gone straight to him. And then one final thing. It was said that, after having denounced him and then, immediately after his arrest, having recanted, asking that he be released, Colomba had backtracked yet again a few weeks later, declaring that he had changed his story because he was frightened about what might happen to his children. He was frightened that Barone might harm his children.

I covered my eyes for a second, suddenly feeling terribly tired.

There was nothing else. Now I just wanted to get out of there. I thanked the young archivist, helped him to put everything back, and left. Outside, the chill air lashed my face and I pulled my scarf tight as I walked away, almost running; I had tears in my eyes and a glowering ache in my chest. The obscenity of that sentence was clinging to me like something revolting. For the first time, I was angry with Colomba, an anger that almost frightened me; and for the very first time, like a tidal wave rushing up through my body, I felt an infinite sadness for my father.

I had a family, and by extension a childhood, both unorthodox and happy. I grew up in a forest of adults, almost none of them my blood relatives, and all of whom contributed in some way to making me what I am, filling my life with affection, with delightful and mysterious contrasts, and with images which have endured to this day, their intensity undimmed.

Even my very earliest memory – the first recollection I can dig up and place with any precision among the earliest flickers of conscious memory – relates to one of those adults. I am in a street on a hill, a very steep city lane, possibly in Istanbul, so I must be three years old; and on the other side of the street I can see Misa smiling at me, having stopped, perhaps to photograph something, or to wait for me. Nothing else remains from either before or after that briefest of hazy instants, but there it is: the remotest spot my memory reaches.

There was Nina who, when I was very tiny, conducted ferocious pedagogical experiments in metalinguistics on me with my mother's help. (For example, they presented me with the words 'train' and 'caterpillar' and asked me which was longer: train, I said, because everyone knows that trains are longer than caterpillars; and with scientific rigour, they took careful notes.) Sometimes I slept over at Nina's house and we chatted away in the dark and I told her stories. I often paid visits to her family in the countryside, and we spent long hours playing in the garden, where there were new kittens every spring, and rabbits and dogs. (Her sisters still enjoy teasing me about my reciprocated adoration of a particularly excitable puppy called Agostino, and about how earnestly I insisted he was my brother, 'Agostino è mio fratello.')

There was my uncle, my mother's brother, a tall, thin man

with weather-beaten skin, who rode me around standing on the crossbar of his bicycle, and who taught me the names of plants and trees, and with whom I shared what has – apart from books – been the greatest and most enduring passion of my life: birds, and above all canaries, which he kept in a large aviary in the courtyard. Every spring he would select a pair to be set to breed in a breeding cage; and the first egg that appeared in the concave little nest would be taken off and put away in a small cotton-wool-lined box and rotated a couple of times a day so that the yolk didn't stick to the shell, and then the same thing was done with all of the others, up to and including the very last egg, which was easy to identify because it was bright blue, and at that point they could all be put back in beneath their mother to be incubated, which meant that they would all be born on the same day and none of them would be bigger than the others and risk crushing the weakest of them or stealing all of his food; and then, thirteen days later, the hatching, and the first cheeps, and the ritual of preparing the mashed feed for the nestlings, and each and every time it was a formidable and thrilling miracle. Of all the books I've ever read, the one I have reread the greatest number of times is probably the *Enciclopedia dei Canarini*, which – when I was, at a guess, nine or ten – my uncle solemnly presented to me one day, with the dedication: 'To Marta, who is a great breeder of canaries'. I took it everywhere I went, and read and reread it, always with the same spasm of pleasure, saving my favourite sections for last so that the enjoyment to be savoured was protracted.

There was Arlette, the Waldensian, who used to take me up into the mountains, and with whom my mother and I lived for the whole of one summer when there was building work being done on our flat. And one evening a bat flew into the house and we tried to catch it using a broom and a colander, and I secretly hoped I'd be allowed to keep it and raise it as my own. Arlette who took me up to Torre Pellice to stay with her parents who seemed to belong in an ancient fairy tale; Arlette who, when I was older, lent me an infinite number of history books.

There was Teresa, who had lived through great drama and

was scared of a great many things, but was always fun to be with and full of life, and eccentric and exuberant, and who claimed to have been the first person ever to have seen me – during an ultrasound scan for which she was present – as well as being indirectly responsible for my existence because it was she who had introduced my parents.

There were Misa and Ester and their beautiful daughter Altea, who was seven years older than me and for whom I nurtured a profound and reciprocated devotion. We went to France in their camper van, and to Portugal, Spain, Holland and Turkey; the camper van remains the most enchanting and sorely missed of all my childhood idylls. I used to sleep in a little bed which was made up for me every night on top of a panel that folded down over the hob; and when I grew too big for it and couldn't sleep there any more, I wept inconsolably over that lost hob, that symbol – now and for ever – of the horrors of growing up.

And then there were, and there are, many other adults. (All of them are still around.)

I loved them very much and they loved me, and they happily tolerated my quirks and caprices. For the sake of example: the imaginary elephant enclosure which I had, at one stage, set up behind the camper van in an area large enough to contain (rather obviously) three elephants, and which accompanied us all the way across Portugal. Whenever anyone forgot about my pachyderms and strolled distractedly up to the back of the camper van, I had conniptions: 'You're treading on the elephants!' I would remind them bitterly. And so they all acquired the habit of skirting round it at a distance, and to this day convulse with laughter when they remind me of the other guests at a campsite, or other drivers parked in a lay-by or at a service station, who bewilderedly watched them make their inexplicable detours behind the van, as though there were a portable Indian burial ground down there, not to be disturbed if terrible curses were not to rain down on future generations.

In a collection of Beppe Fenoglio's experiments in translation, I once came across a poem by Gerard Manley Hopkins – 'In the

Valley of the Elwy' – and the opening couplet, which I still have off by heart, went like this: 'I remember a house where all were good / To me, God knows, deserving no such thing.' When I read that, I cried. It seemed to me to be the most incisive and most perfect description of what all these people had been to me – these people who had welcomed me, had loved me, and had each given me a piece of their world. My loved ones.

My father was in some ways quite separate from all this. I thought of him as being an entity apart, which he certainly wanted to be. It hurt me that the people I loved didn't love him. Or no longer loved him. He didn't act like any other adult I knew, and he didn't act like a parent: he was ruleless, irresponsible and irrational. It was very evident that the little girl confronting him was, as far as he was concerned, the most puzzling of enigmas. We didn't really know how to talk to one another, or how to be together. While my mother and I shared everything – all the plays to be put on, all the books to be read, all the long stories invented together on car journeys, our private languages, our sense of humour – with him I didn't really have any points of contact. The only language we shared was that of Greek myths.

I owned a set of picture books, published by Dami Editore with gorgeous illustrations from the 1970s by the enchantingly named Libico Maraja, and I read them compulsively: there was the *Iliad*, the *Odyssey*, the *Aeneid*, and a whole series of mythological tales.

He was ardently in love with Greek mythology and knew its every twist and turn, all the labyrinthine kinships (which satisfied his congenital need for gossip). The same was true of the *Iliad* and the *Odyssey*, but he wasn't particularly enthusiastic about the *Aeneid* (apart from Palinurus, Aeneas's helmsman who drowned in the night because he fell asleep at the helm, as my father took pains to remind me every time we drove past Cape Palinuro on our way to or back from a holiday. Poor, poor Palinurus!) When I was five or six years old, I used to trot over to his flat (in the attic) with my picture books in my backpack and, familiar with them though he was, read him the same stories hundreds of times over: the ignoble Theseus, merry old Dionysus who was born of a thigh, Orpheus and Eurydice, Perseus and Medusa, Hector and Andromache (and little Astyanax who was thrown from the walls of Troy), Odysseus, Penelope, Telemachus, Polyphemus, Laertes, Zeus, Poseidon, Hephaestus, Heracles, and so on and so forth. We had a favourite goddess – Athena – and a shared aversion for the same lowlifes: Theseus (obviously), that other recreant, Jason, and inconsequential Paris. Out of an aesthetic predilection for losers, he preferred Hector to Achilles. But my father's real hero, beating the others by a country mile, was Odysseus.

To both of us, these outlandish, admirable and dreadful figures felt every bit as real as close relatives with rather eccentric habits. That was how we talked about them – deriding, admiring or questioning the motives behind their madcap feats, while we ate lunch in the little kitchen with the window that looked out onto the rooftops, or while we walked down the street. Between one building and the next, out popped the Hydra's throbbing heads; the ambiguous centaur Nessus winked at us from beneath the linden trees in the park; the cobblestone pavement burst open and out jumped Hades with his gloomy chariot, come to fetch Persephone who was sitting in a flowerbed. In summertime, we watched repeats of the 1968 version of *Odisseo* on televisions in other people's kitchens, always sprawled anxiously across the kitchen table as if we didn't know exactly what was going to happen next. It was normally Irene Papas, with her kohl-rimmed eyes and almost the same surname as Enrico Maria Papes. Enrico Maria Papes was the drummer from the Giganti – another regular fixture of our summers ...

One time in what must have been April or May, he came to pick me up from school (I think I was still at nursery school) and, with an air of great mystery, walked me over to his old wreck of a car. I peered through the window: there were two grey tabby kittens climbing all over the seats. I have no idea where he got them from, and I don't know why it ever occurred to him – he who could barely look after himself – to take on the responsibility of two little lives, but that ludicrous, adorable gesture was all for my benefit: it was a shy and clumsy attempt to make me happy. Looking back on them now – the man and the little girl standing on the sunlit pavement in Piazzetta Maria Teresa and peering into the olive-green Fiat Ritmo – with an adult's detachment I see other things too: his desire to play a part in my world, which wasn't his; an attempt to make the two sunless little rooms he lived in feel more like a home where there would always be something lovely waiting for me.

Naturally, I was beside myself with excitement. Two kittens! Not just one! I must have seemed drunk. That day we took the kittens with us (still happily exploring the inside of the car) to Imbarchini, a riverside bar in the Valentino park – a white building with red window frames and shutters, and long tables under a pergola that was swathed in Virginia creeper, which also curled around the wooden fencing; and everywhere bushes of pink oleander, grown so big and so heavy that they bowed down over the water. One entered via a little gate beneath an arched sign which was painted green, and then down a short flight of steps with big rocks to either side of them. While my father chatted to someone (there was always someone he knew there; only recently, I discovered that he had once worked there for a couple of months, as a spare pair of hands, when he'd needed to scrabble together some extra cash), I sat off to one side among the pots of geraniums and nasturtiums, playing with the kittens and fetching them back whenever they strayed too far or got too close to the river. The water was green. Everything was green and murmurous.

**

Like all beautiful and ludicrous things, the kittens didn't last very long. The minute he was old enough to feel the first stirrings of love, the boy kitten escaped out on to the rooftops and never came back; a few weeks later the female was given away to a cat-owning friend with a bigger flat – where our kitten would live a long and noble life.

But I do remember that day.

It was February when I finally met up with Agata. I was in Turin for a creative writing workshop with a class of schoolchildren, and we arranged to meet towards the end of the afternoon when she left the office. Making my way to the appointment, I had no expectations. In the sense that I didn't know what to expect.

From my childhood visits to her home I remembered that from her balcony one could see the enormously tall bell tower of a church with a bronze angel at the top of its spire, and that in springtime she made delicious fresh-herb omelettes, and that her face and her voice always exuded a gentle melancholy. I also had very clear memories of her eldest daughter, who was born when I was six years old. When my father went to live with his new partner, Dora, he stopped meeting up with Agata and her new partner almost entirely, and so I, too, had hardly seen them after that. Except at the family parties I've already mentioned – because our friend Misa was her partner's older brother.

I really didn't know Agata, and she didn't know me, apart from what she remembered of me as a little girl. I could hazard a guess at what she thought of me, though, and the idea was an uncomfortable one. I knew that she, like others, thought that I hadn't loved my father as much as I should have. That I hadn't loved him in the right way, let's say. She probably couldn't begin to imagine how sad it had been (all that long, tiring, terrible sadness). And perhaps she thought I had no right – I, of all people, the unsatisfactory daughter – to turn up asking to be told a story about him. What little she could know about me was conjecture and hearsay. And it was this, more than anything, that made me uneasy.

So I was frightened she wouldn't trust me. But also that she wouldn't remember things precisely enough, or that she wouldn't want to. I was afraid I was being invasive; I was afraid I might say something inopportune. And yet, that shiver of anticipation, that sense of something beckoning ...

I wouldn't mention Colomba again, I thought: that had been a mistake. I wouldn't tell her about the obscene phrase I had read at the archive. I wouldn't even talk about Mure Galiani, or the other tenebrous, silent figures who moved about in the shadowy background of that doleful operetta. I would leave it up to her to decide what to tell me. And what not to.

She was waiting for me on the corner of Via Garibaldi and Via Sant'Agostino. She had a chequered coat and blonder hair than I remembered, cut in a bob. She walked towards me with – to my surprise – joy in her face, and squeezed my hands. I greeted her slightly clumsily. An awkwardness she immediately diffused by suggesting a nearby *pasticceria* where we'd be able to talk.

It was one of those nineteenth-century cafés with dark wood panelling and shelves full of jars and golden biscuit tins and shinily wrapped chocolates, cafés which – in Turin – all look alike and all glow with the same strangely cloudy light. We sat at a little round table set slightly apart from the others in a *sala* with chairs and banquettes thickly upholstered in emerald-green velvet. An unctuous waiter brought over menus. At another table two elegant women in their early seventies lowered their heads into the stream of their gossip, their hair puffed into elaborate coifs, their necks vaguely like vultures'. It was a rather odd setting for what I'd come to hear, I thought.

Agata studied me. The expression on her face was benevolent, encouraging even. I had expected her to be chary, but she wasn't. The glasses widened her already-gentle myopic eyes, those big, very slightly upturned grey-green eyes which shone with an emotion that had something maternal to it.

We both ordered tea. She insisted I have something to eat and I opted for a carnival pastry I didn't really want (it was the season for them), more for the sake of having something to do with my hands than anything else.

Once the waiter had gone off with our orders, she told me I

was looking more than ever like a young version of my paternal grandmother; and that at my father's funeral, seeing me for the first time in twenty years, her mother had said the same thing. I shrugged. I had no idea what my grandmother had looked like as a young woman. A few months later I would come across a photo of my grandmother and wouldn't see any particular resemblance. There are only two faces mine resembles.

The waiter brought over the teapot, cups, a plate with the pastries. He fluttered off.

Agata paused while she put the teabags in the pot. She seemed to be mulling something over, then she said: 'I want to tell you about the first time I ever saw you, Marta. You were in your crib in the hospital nursery. You were a day old. And your mummy and daddy were standing at the viewing window, hugging each another.'

She mimed the gesture. I hurriedly looked away. I could feel the sting of tears on their way. This wasn't what I was there for. I didn't want to hear about myself, I just wanted to hear the story behind the trial. Nothing else. This wasn't part of the deal. (More than the image, I think, what upset me was the – for me – unfamiliar combination of words, 'your mummy and daddy', which I had never heard spoken quite like that.) Reasoning it through, a long time afterwards, I realised that the scene she was describing must have happened at least two or three days later than she thought: my mother had been very unwell after the birth and couldn't have been up and about so early on. But in Agata's memory the episode – which she must, in any case, have witnessed – had been brought forward; two separate episodes had fused, out of a desire for it to be true, out of tenderness, for the sake of narrative effect. And this in itself taught me something about the way in which human beings remember things, about the grey area where facts mesh with memory to the point at which, looking back, we can no longer tell them apart.

She continued: 'And the first time I ever saw your father he was the same age you are now.'

I looked back up into her face.

'Really?'

'Yes. How old are you? You're almost twenty-seven, aren't you?'

'Next month.'

'Well, there you go. He was twenty-seven and I was eighteen.'

She slid her hand off the table, as though making room for the incoming ghosts.

'It was the fifteenth of September, 1973. I walked around a corner, and there he was.'

And that was exactly how it happened, more or less. Agata came from a working-class but well-educated family with a complicated history of sacrifices made and unresolved griefs. Her father worked for Lancia, engine testing. As a young man he had studied at the Politecnico, but then it was bombed and he had had to break off his studies and had never completed them, after the war, because a series of infelicitous events meant he had to find work. She had started work at fifteen, for a relative. She was a graphic designer in a studio specialising mostly in car ads. To begin with she wasn't even paid for it, then she had gone on strike with the others and the firm had been forced to give her a monthly salary.

'My designs were good,' she said, and I heard the shade of resentment in her voice. And the shade of the shade of the resentment her father had felt before her.

Sometime later I saw some photographs of Agata from back then. She had had wavy hair, light brown, not quite reaching her shoulders, and a tousled fringe; pencil-thin eyebrows; a gamine face dominated by those huge sad eyes, often half-hidden behind big tinted glasses. On the rare occasions when she was smiling, it was a hint of a smile – distrait. It looked like her thoughts were always elsewhere.

The fifteenth of September 1973, then. As the meteorological archives inform us: mean daily temperature 20 °C, dew point 16.2 °C. It was a Saturday, so she wasn't at work. She was on her way to join the protest march against the coup in Chile, marching for the first time in her life, because she felt it was important to be there, because she sensed the horror of those hours.

So the young Agata walked around the corner into the piazza, and just beyond the corner there was a group of people gathered around someone who was talking. They were all smiling and asking him things, and voices called out to him from here and there in the group, Barone, Barone, and that was how Agata heard his name for the very first time. They were organising vaccinations for the comrades who were going down to Naples to help out in the districts infected with cholera, and he was directing the operation.

What must he have looked like, the young man who wasn't yet my father, that day? You and I don't know that, reader. But we can fantasise.

The only clue we have that this is him is a sky-blue jersey shining out from the murky haze of Agata's memory like a blot of light imprinted on a retina behind closed eyes. He must have had short hair, sideburns, maybe a moustache. He would have been wearing a rather creased pair of overlarge trousers, like he always did. Clumpy shoes. But there would also have been that particular form of grace in his smiling face, in the dance-like quality of his movements as he turned from one interlocutor to the next.

Ever since, whenever I happen to pass – or make a deliberate detour – via that spot in Piazza Arbarello where the pavement widens out below the cream and blue-grey of the houses, I slow my pace and wait for the rays of that still-vivid image to fan out and reach me, vicariously, through time, and I think: This is where it all began.

We have no other details of how it began and developed – this singular love story; Agata maintained a certain reserve when narrating it to me, and in effect it was her business, not mine. But it seems the beginning was rather slow and difficult, among other things because not long after they met, but before they'd properly become a couple, there was 'the Via Artisti business', as Agata called it, and – from the way she said the words – that seemed to be something terrible. I didn't interrupt her to ask her what she meant, though, because I could see she was making a great effort to tell me everything in the right order; instead, as happens to all of us when recalling far-off events, it came back to her in waves, in terse, random details, and as a result she jumped back and forth in time. So it was in this way, in waves and billows, that I learned that my father had taken part in the Battle of Valle Giulia in 1968, and that he had been one of the key figures in the student movement in those months; that before this, when he first arrived at the university in Rome, in 1964, he had joined one of the Christian organisations involved in running after-school clubs in deprived suburbs. And how it was that he had progressed from *that* to communism remained one of the mysteries of his life pre-Agata. Then – and Agata didn't remember when – he had come up to Turin. He had been sent, she said. He had been sent by what she referred to as 'the PCIM-L'. The *Partito Comunista Italiano Marxista-Leninista*, aka *Servire il Popolo*. Serve the People.

Here, I couldn't resist intervening.

'My father was in Serve the People?' I asked, stunned.

'And so was I,' replied Agata, with a tight smile.

Not that I knew a great deal about the party. I had just heard them mentioned from time to time as a sect-like group of extremists, almost comical in their fanatical zealotry. I mean, they used to call them '*Servire il pollo*' (serve the chicken). It was the furthest thing from my extravagantly disorganised father that I could possibly imagine.

'More than that,' continued Agata. 'Your father was one of the party cadres. They sent him to Turin because it was the city where all the factories were, and because the ethos of the PCIM-L was that intellectuals had to "humble themselves".' She pronounced the words with unconcealed scorn. 'They had to abandon their studies and anything else they did and dedicate themselves exclusively to the party. They had to abandon their "bourgeois" habits. They were made to do the lowliest of jobs. When I met him he was washing trams for a living. Him, of all people! He'd taken every single one of his exams early, he could have been a graduate by then, he could have been a qualified doctor, and he was washing down trams, and apart from the allowance the party gave him, every penny he earned went straight to them.'

She told me that the PCIM-L demanded that its richer members donate part of their patrimony to the party coffers, and that one of my father's friends – someone I would meet, years later – had sold the house his parents had bought for him. There were people who had made over everything, had donated literally everything they owned, had handed over their share of inheritances; and all this without being in any way obliged to – because the revolution was imminent. But even the poorer members paid in a percentage of their monthly earnings. No one was to possess too many belongings, just the indispensable (at one point, instructions were even circulated regarding the number of bedsheets one should have in the house), and the militants had to live like ascetics so that they would be true to the message they preached. Indefatigable souls charged with collecting the dues passed regularly from house to house to retrieve the monthly offering and to accept, or delicately extort, the possessions to be 'collectivised', which would then be sold off to fund the party. But every so often the collectivised objects – washing machines, family silver, hairdryers – were spotted in the homes of party officials. Or so it was whispered.

The party's leader and founder, Brandirali, issued directives regarding more or less every aspect of the militants' personal lives: their wardrobes, which had to be limited to a minimal number of garments, as plain as was possible; artistic tastes ('If you create something, you must ask yourself: does it serve the people or does it not serve the people?'): Agata was told that her drawings were worthless because they didn't portray the proletariat, but then they used her poster designs over and over again, as soon as she'd fallen in with the party command; their sexual habits (if anyone had an extramarital affair they were chucked straight out, no ifs or buts), their most private of thoughts, their recondite and therefore bourgeois sentiments, were the subject of terrifying sessions of criticism and self-criticism which turned into what were effectively collegial trials, almost always ending with the identification of a scapegoat, who was expected to express profound remorse or risk expulsion. During these sessions, many of them ended up in floods of tears, finding it all too much to bear, and yet most of them remained desperately loyal to whatever it was that ... whatever was it? Even Agata couldn't begin to explain.

'That was why we got married, you know. The party obliged us to. Because we weren't allowed relationships outside marriage. They told me I had to do it so that I would understand what life was like for the women of the proletariat. I *was* a woman of the proletariat, but that detail apparently escaped them. When I finished work for the day and the women in the party who had children were off somewhere doing something, I had to look after their children so that *they* could be free to pursue their political activities.'

I stared at her.

'They were worse than the worst of the Catholics. Much worse! They even had communist weddings.'

At that point she started giggling, and so did I, because the idea of a communist wedding really was just too funny. But then she suddenly stopped.

'I know all of this must seem ridiculous to you, and it was. It was so silly that it still embarrasses me. But back then we thought it was as good a way as ... I dunno. The party seemed ... practical. We were involved in the campaigns for housing, in the factory workers' campaigns. We were forever handing out material aimed at the People – whoever that was supposed to be – explaining how their situation could change for the better. And at the end of the day that was all we really wanted: we wanted everyone to have a roof over their heads and the same chances in life; we wanted the rich not to be so obscenely rich, and the poor to have dignified lives and to be able to become whatever they wanted to become. They said it would take seven years for the revolution to happen. Seven years. A magic number. Like in fairy tales, like in legends. And we truly thought it would. There were places where it was already happening – so far away that they might just as well have been imaginary, but it was happening. It wasn't so very improbable. We believed in it. We thought the party would be a motor for it, and instead it was just a mindless machine which chewed us all up and we never even noticed. I was eighteen when I got married. The party even took the bits and pieces of linen my grandmother had left me for my bottom drawer; you only need one bedsheet, they said. My father didn't approve of me getting married so young, and he refused to give me more than a million lire, which went straight to the party. But one of them turned up to collect my father's gold Marengo, too. He had bought three of them, one for me, one for my sister, and one for my brother, as an investment. Like a fool, I'd told them about it. And he handed it over. There was hardly anyone at the wedding, just our closest relatives, and no one was happy. That evening, when we got back to that awful flat that we were going to live in for a bit, owning nothing, owning only a set of cutlery, I wept. I spent the whole evening weeping. We didn't have anything to eat. A couple of days later our friends organised a supper for us, and they brought their guitars to make a party of it, afterwards, in the park; and most importantly, they brought food. They brought us something to eat. I'd been so hungry. For days.'

Tears began to run down her face. I wasn't sure what to do. Hold her hand? I shuffled in my seat, then I touched her arm. She shook her head as if to say it's nothing, don't worry, and she dried her cheeks.

She picked up where she'd left off, saying that that year – it was 1974 – they had gone to live in Villar Perosa, a village in the Province of Turin. They had been sent there – again – by the party. And it had been very hard. Since Agata had a salary, the PCIM-L had immediately withdrawn my father's party-official's stipend. They had no possessions. My father's relatives bought them a few pieces of furniture and a cooker, which arrived several weeks after the move. For all those weeks they lived as though they were on a two-room island, without a table, without a bed, tossed into that desolate space just like their few, illogical possessions, like the cutlery they had been given as a wedding present without even having a drawer to put it in or plates off which to eat. But in any case, they spent very little time in the house. They didn't have what could legitimately have been called a married life, given that, what with her job and the bits and pieces of day labour he did and their duties as militants (the nature of which I continued to grasp only vaguely), they were always apart or surrounded by other people. But they loved one another very much, with great simplicity. Right from the start it had struck me that when she talked about him it was never as though he were someone with whom she had shared a romantic bond, but with the fierce tenderness one feels for a much-loved brother. She said that he was wonderful to be around, that he always did his best to lift her spirits when all the sadness around which they tiptoed suddenly outwelled, now and then, like leakage from a broken pipe. Yes, said Agata, he could have infected a lump of stone with that enthusiasm of his; he was a 'good man'. And in fact he had a multitude of friends, even people very different from him, and very distant from the PCIM-L. Agata admired his sense of duty, his earnest desire to better the world and to throw himself into any context where there was a need for someone to make a nuisance of themselves in order to improve things. But above all she admired his intelligence ('He knew how to explain things to people'). And the waste of that intelligence was, to her mind, intolerable. It was she, she told me, who had insisted he finally finish his degree. He couldn't abandon his true vocation: he had to become a doctor.

He wrote his thesis sitting at the kitchen table late in the evenings when he got back from work or from the party's local branch office, using a typewriter he had somehow procured, and sleepily, fiercely engrossed. Agata would go off to bed and he would still be there, with a blanket on his shoulders because it was always cold, surrounded by books, untidy notes and coils of smoke which hovered above his head in the perfunctory light of the table lamp. Sometimes she found him sleeping in the same position the following morning, when she got up at the crack of dawn to catch the bus that took her into Turin and the office.

The thesis was on the connection between cancers – particularly bronchopulmonary and pleural tumours – and the social environment. He had wanted to dedicate a few pages to the IPCA paint factory in Ciriè; the base product they used was aniline, which caused bladder cancer. Allegations had been made and ignored for decades. Dozens of workers had died in the past seven years, and a further thirty or so were ill. They called them the *pissabrut*, the men with red piss. But he had had to make do with a couple of sentences.

'He went from house to house, trying to interview people who'd worked there and had fallen ill, but back then it still wasn't being talked about. The manslaughter case brought against the IPCA directors didn't come to trial until a few years later, and none of them opened their doors to him. But he kept going back, time and time again. He was on his own for his graduation, poor thing. I couldn't be there, because I had to go to work.'

It was beginning to get late and Agata was suddenly in a hurry. She briefly explained that towards the end of 1975 Brandirali had disbanded the party (and then joined the anti-liberal Catholic movement, *Comunione e Liberazione*, and eventually moved on to the far right), and that my father had been one of the instigators of the disbanding, at one of the long, exhausting, hysterical meetings of the previous months during which many of them had already decided to leave. Their self-imposed Leviathan was dead: they were, finally, free.

She would tell me all the rest of it, everything that happened in the years that followed, another time, and in the meantime she would give me a few other names if they came to mind. The teapot had been empty for a while, the vulture ladies had left. There was just one more thing to ask her: what had she meant by 'the Via Artisti business'?

She looked at me, astonished.

'You don't know? They never told you about it? Not even your mother?'

They'd never told me about any of the rest of it, for that matter (and later on, when I asked my mother, it turned out she didn't know anything either, nor had she known about the PCIM-L or Valle Giulia). So I shrugged, expectantly. Her face tightened.

'Oh ... it's a horrible story. Horrible.'

And she told me.

When we walked out of the café it had just gone seven and it was dark. The pedestrianised street was, as usual, busy with foot traffic, but there was less noise than normal. I knew it well, that street; and yet the sensation I had was the same I had felt – but a more powerful version of it – the day after reading the notice of appeal, when I had walked down to Piazza Vittorio; as though it were suddenly transfigured and sibylline, as though something had descended irreversibly between me and the things I had always considered comprehensible. Agata and I set off towards Piazza Castello.

At one point she stopped and said to me, 'You know why I've told you all of this? Because I wanted you to begin to understand ... to see the difference between what your father was beforehand and what he was later. What you knew him as.'

I didn't say anything. I was exhausted.

'Back then he was an enchanting man,' she added. 'So happy. Everyone, when we were anywhere near him, was happy by association.'

We resumed our walk. Agata was sad and uneasy, her face twisting in the shadows. We stopped in the pool of light beneath a streetlamp when we reached the castle. There was no one else around. She squeezed my arm and asked, again: 'But why do you want to know about the trial? Why? That wasn't him, it wasn't what he was.'

'Yes, I know,' I lied (I didn't know, I knew less now than I had before: actually, it felt like I'd never known anything about anything). 'I know there's no great mystery.'

'Yes,' she said, almost tenderly. 'There's no great mystery.'

Agata walked off towards the tram, which was about to arrive at its stop; she kept turning round to look back at me. I waved, waited until she'd climbed in, and went home.

In a way, Agata had led me completely off-piste with her strange, fractured story, which, somewhere far-off and nocturnal, had ignited phosphorescent glimmers the possibility of which I had never even contemplated. And now I felt an almost painful need to flesh out what she had told me. Absurd as it might sound, it felt as though I needed to confirm that my father had truly existed, that his youth had happened, that somewhere or other, long ago, he had once done something – even something prosaic – which had left some trace and could reach me through time.

I did find something, three days later. Late on a foggy evening. I was alone in my flat in Milan, and from the window, through the murk, I could just about make out the few windows where the lights were still on in the building in front of ours. ('I wonder if Milan still exists; / my grandfather told me about Milan, a city of witches,' wrote the poet.)

My father's name produced no results on any of the search engines I tried, apart from the conferences on troubled adolescents at which he'd spoken in the last few years of his life. Then I tried searching the online archives of *La Stampa*, selecting a date range from 1968 to 1990. Twenty-four results. I inhaled.

The first articles to come up were about his arrest. The very first had appeared in the local news section for Turin in the paper's evening edition on Tuesday, 22 June 1982. *Is he really a Front Liner? Furloughed Fiat worker under arrest for participation in armed band.* 'Early this morning carabinieri in Turin arrested 37-year-old furloughed Fiat worker Leonardo Barone, currently resident in Via V., in connection with ongoing investigations into Front Line. Barone is a well-known figure on the workers' movement scene in Turin and over the past few years has been a stalwart of campaigns against furloughing and redundancies.

The arrest warrant issued by Substitute Procurator A.B. accuses Barone of violating art. 306 (contributing to the formation of or participating in an armed band), aggravated by additional offences. The warrant cites a series of crimes that the factory worker is purported to have committed with the intention of "violently undermining the economic and social order of the State", including the distribution of printed material advocating armed insurrection, possession of firearms and explosives, and even an armed robbery. All of this emerged from statements made by a "repentant" terrorist whose name has not, however, been made public. We also understand that, despite the number and gravity of the presumed offences, the warrant classes the arrest as "opportune" rather than "obligatory". Meanwhile, the *Centro di Documentazione* in Via Plava has released a statement "confirming" that Leonardo Barone is "an acknowledged spearhead of the movement".'

This was followed by an advert for a shop with a new range of carpets and paints: a cheerful housepainter with a triangular newspaper hat was using his brush to complete the company logo. And then: Happening Today and Tomorrow: Continuing our series of events focusing on 'Women. Our health, our problems', join us at 8 p.m. tomorrow at the Anna Frank school hall at 15 Via Scoletellaro to discuss 'Contraception, abortion and educating women for health'. Tonight at 9 p.m., venue Edy Franchetti school hall, Via Randaccio, a lecture on 'Cultural Expressions in Piedmontese'. 'Why purchase bathroom fittings in a shop? Buy direct from the factory! A matching mirror and tiles and made-to-measure shower cabinets could all be yours. Wholesale prices. D. Bathroom Mirrors, at the 17km route marker on the Rivoli-Avigliana A-road.' And below that, a large photo of a car: 'Some Saab it, most don't. Fiorauto. A guarantee of exclusivity.'

The day afterwards they had published a longer piece which went into more detail. *Factory worker with degree in medicine: was he in FL's health-professionals' brigade?* From both pages of the paper out stared the same black-and-white photo of my father, looking round-eyed and rather lost, his mouth half-open as though he were in the middle of saying something. Then there were various other articles revealing additional details regarding the charges being brought, the time of day at which the heavily armed carabinieri had burst into the house (six o'clock in the morning), Agata's version of events ('his wife, a 25-year-old office worker'), and defensive references to that mysterious *Centro di Documentazione* in Via Plava. They called him the worker-medic, or the metalworker with a medical degree. Then there was the indictment, on 30 December 1983; the headline read, *All the charges and one of the Rovigo escapees*. There was also the news that he had been acquitted, on 9 June 1988.

I leaned back in my chair and sucked in my cheeks, musing. He had told me he'd left his job at the hospital after being arrested. I did know he had been a factory worker for a few years: my mother had mentioned it, as an example of the kind of ridiculous lies he told. (To start with he hadn't even told his wife or his friends that he was no longer practising medicine. He left the house each morning pretending to go into hospital, and went into the factory instead. For at least six months, until, somehow or other, they all found out.) She had heard about it via Misa and Ester, who were friends of my father's back then. But if, at the point when he was arrested for participation in an armed band, he was already a factory worker – and had been doing it long enough to have ended up furloughed – then what he'd told me wasn't true. So why had he left the hospital? And when?

There were, inevitably, numerous articles about Via Artisti. I read them all carefully and reluctantly, one after another. And then odd bits and pieces: various arrests for picketing and for 'criminal affronts'. (In one photo, from a criminal defamation case that had followed an uncommonly moronic incident, he was sitting, in court, next to his co-defendant – a teacher who was one of his party comrades – and was laughing, with his head bowed. She just looked unbelievably bored.) There was even a 1978 arrest for subversive conspiracy – which obviously came to nothing – where it was claimed that he was one of Workers' Autonomy's two Turin-based leaders.

The night wore on. At one o'clock, I remember hearing the clatter of the last tram of the night: together with the first one of the morning, at five, it regularly bookended my chronic insomnia. And I continued searching. In *Unità*, whose online archive was still available at the time, I found just one brief reference, dated 17 March 1968: it described an episode from the day before, in Rome, when a group of neo-fascists had occupied the Sapienza university and had hurled desks and chairs out of the windows and on to the left-wing students who were protesting down below. That was the day on which Oreste S., who would go on to found Workers' Power, was left with a badly injured spine. The other person named as having been injured, in his case with less serious head wounds, was the twenty-two-year-old medical student Leonardo Barone. Our family, it turns out, had an august tradition of cracked skulls. Suddenly I remembered a scene I couldn't quite place (but it was summertime and I think we were sitting on a bench in a station): my father, laughing, was saying to me, 'My parents didn't realise I was the family's bad apple. My father only found out I was a communist when the fascists whacked me on the head and an article came out in the newspaper. Someone in the town told him about it and he phoned me in hospital and asked me, quite taken aback: "But Leonardo ... but is it *true*?" And I never did work out whether he was talking about my head or the communism.'

The fallout had been less amusing, as I would discover via Dora many years later. His father had immediately stopped sending him money, and to make ends meet he had had to find work as a housepainter. And it didn't stop there: his father broke off all forms of communication. Then again, the family – all of them – had had rather different expectations of the exceptionally gifted little boy whose genius had even been the subject of a gypsy prophesy when his mother was pregnant; the only one of the children to have gone to university ... At the very least a serene, respectable and well-paid career in medicine; a position conferring a certain status. A status which they, by extension, would share.

But instead.

I switched off the computer and the room was left pitch

black. I leaned over to switch on the bedside lamp, lowered the shutters and, with a series of mechanical gestures, pulled open the bed; then I slipped on my pyjamas, lay down, and – having switched the light back off – stared at the invisible ceiling. So there it was then. Those confused, disconnected fragments were all the written material I had. The sum total. A story as vague and evanescent as a piece of land seen from a ship by night, when only its dim outline is guessable, and then it drifts away, leaving us forever wondering which country it really was. Or like a hypnogogic vision – those fleeting hallucinations in the final seconds before one falls asleep when, somewhere between your eyelid and the space beyond, strange motifs unfurl across the bedroom wall, or monstrous figures appear, or the features of an object are distorted in the semi-darkness.

I had the impression that I hadn't got any closer, that I was actually drifting further away from that hazy night-time country. I could still only see its outline. Above all, I was thinking of Via Artisti. And it continued to swell and stiffen in my chest like a physical pain. Was it really possible I'd never noticed any sign, in him, of that past? How much had I been unaware of? How many questions could I have asked? Would it have changed anything? There was a sentence I'd scribbled down just a few months earlier, for the now-dead novel. I'd been planning to get my protagonist to say it: *Perhaps she should have paid more attention.* And now, because fate has a taste for dark humour, it came back to me with a whole new meaning, and hooked itself into my side like a thorn I would never get rid of. I sat up with a start, switched the computer back on, and retrieved that blurry, startled-looking, barely legible photo. Who are you? I thought, and that thought was almost a howl. I closed the lid of the laptop again and got back into bed. But I lay in the dark with my eyes open for a very long time.

We'd been at war with one another for years. Round about the time when he went to live with Dora and apparently decided to become a Proper Father, he had changed. All of a sudden he was petulant and boorish; when he spoke to me it was almost always in a pointlessly aggressive tone; he flew into continual rages, as fierce as they were senseless, about rules that had never previously existed and which he himself didn't obey. He couldn't stand me wanting to be left alone when I was staying with them, and the fact that every so often I would wander off to spend an hour or so in my own company, as I was used to doing at home, or anywhere else, for that matter: he took it as a personal affront. Any attempt I made at pleasing him, or at making amends for a presumed (and usually entirely imaginary) error, ended up, in any case, being wrong. I much preferred the distracted semi-delinquent father of former times. This one was despotic, irrational and capricious: more a parody version of an adult than a proper adult. I didn't understand and I didn't know what to do. I was the same as ever: why was that suddenly no longer good enough?

During the holidays in August – the longest consecutive period I spent with him each year – we would spend three or four weeks at Dora's holiday home in Calabria, and there was hardly ever a moment's truce. Three weeks, when you are nine years old, are infinite. My desperation was infinite. And that was when I discovered that almost nobody is remotely interested in children's misery. Most people consider it an irrelevance, a minor inconvenience, or don't even notice it. And the more miserable I was, the angrier he got. It wasn't fair that I was sad when I was with him. That was an affront, too.

Actually, I think he frequently regretted the way he spoke to me, the terrible words he spewed at me when he was in a rage, but he had no idea how to reverse the damage. He would often come to the door of the room I'd closed myself in so that I could cry in the dark after the latest tirade, and he would stand there and murmur, 'Marzolina,' little Marta, the nickname my mother had given me and that he used, too, when he was in the mood for demonstrativeness. 'Marzolina, come on, come into the other room.' It was the closest he got to saying sorry.

Sometimes, for an hour or two, or even for whole days at a time, he was normal and loving in his own slightly overpowering way, and I clutched at those intervals of transitory peace as though they were our lifeline. But they quickly passed, for unpredictable motives which were often very trivial. I was always on the alert, always miserably anxious.

(But he spent entire nights watching over me – that time I came down with one of my perennial tonsillitises – with the volume turned right down on the little television in the holiday home's kitchen where the sofa bed I slept on was, and when I opened my eyes, delirious with fever, I saw him silhouetted in the darkness, sitting at the table, head on hand, his features faintly illuminated by the images of the film he was watching to keep himself awake.)

The only person in front of whom he held himself back was my mother. He respected her immensely, and I think he was also slightly in awe of her; she was the sound parent, the wise parent. He wanted her to think well of him. Right till the end she was the calming presence in our lives. When she was around – and all it took was for her to be around, gentle and discreet, because she watched our every move and was always quick to pronounce a quiet word of warning if she ever sensed that something was about to snap – a radiant normality descended on the room. When she was around nothing was ever unpleasant or sordid.

At suppers or at parties with his friends, my father would read out my poems and childish stories. I was very embarrassed and knew my mother thought things like this were bad for children and hated ostentation, which increased my discomfort, because even when she wasn't there I was conscious of her disapproval, the disappointment on her face when I was shown off or – excited by the applause – I showed off. But I couldn't help being happy that this side of me, at least, was appreciated. And after all, who doesn't love praise? The fellow guests would let out little cries of delight and my father would swell with pride, he shone with joy. He bragged, to his public, about the precocity of my writing, my intelligence. My intelligence, which was inherited, of course. She's as clever as her father. 'Like father, like daughter,' he would say to me, rhapsodically, and a bluish, poisonous ire would rise up through my legs and invade my whole body, it would fill me up, all the way to my fingertips, all the way to my skull, and all I could think was: I am not like you. I will never be like you.

Then it ebbed, and all that was left was a huge sadness, the awful sense of a defeat which was his as much as mine.

(But still, still, there was the sea. He loved the sea and so did I. Deeply, piercingly, incommunicably. We went off on long expeditions during which we barely exchanged a word. All I could hear was his breath in the snorkel, and my own short gasps. He taught me how to clean the mask with my spit when it clouded over. We pushed on out to places where no one else went, between the cliffs, beyond the promontories, and even further out than that. The world below the surface was all ours, then. A world both alive and ghostly. The muffled, blunted noisy-silence which buzzed in my ears when I dived down. The forests of algae on some of the seabeds, dancing slowly backwards and forwards to the rhythm of the waves. The hollows in the rocks where the sea urchins hid out. The rays of sunlight which cut through the water diagonally and projected trembling rhomboids on to the seafloor. The dark and boundless blue which opened out in front of me whenever I looked out towards the open sea. That effort was a happy effort. Whenever, after a long outing, I collapsed on to the beach, dog-tired, replete, wet hair hanging into my face, and he stroked my head and smiled proudly, I felt good. I felt something that felt like love.)

My childhood came to an abrupt full stop when I was eleven and my unrepressed, ungendered body transformed itself, in the space of a month, into the body of a female, and puberty transformed me into a melancholy, silent, intractable creature, filled with self-loathing and a horror of others. As can be imagined, this did little to improve my already far-from-idyllic relationship with my father. I too became vicious. More and more vicious by the day. I yelled back when he yelled at me. I rose to every bait. I was awash with anger. It ate me up, it swamped me, it cancelled out all rational thoughts; I lost control, just like him, in a monstrous mirror image of his irascibility. Like father, like daughter.

I loathed the person I became in those moments. I hated her as much as and more than I hated him. That wasn't me. I was deeply, constantly ashamed of myself, a shame which gnawed at my bones, which made me want to vanish off the face of the earth. No one could console or help me: I was as guilty as my father. Guiltier even, because I lacked filial respect. Or so those other people seemed to think. The onlookers.

A bad daughter. An unsatisfactory daughter.

At seventeen I made the decision to put an end to all of this. Worn out, I ran away – quite literally – from one of those holidays, surreptitiously catching the train home. We didn't speak to one another for a long time after that. He couldn't forgive me. Me, I found it almost funny. Besides, what sense was there in repeating that lousy pantomime every year, at all costs? Didn't he realise we'd be happier like this, all of us? Even now, I don't understand that violent contradiction between his desire to have me with him for those few weeks and the way he behaved once we were there. I think he didn't understand it either.

And despite it all, he kept a photo of me in a frame on his bedside table. In it, I was fourteen and was reading, with my legs crossed, under a beach umbrella, my face wrinkled up, biting at a fingernail, my hair twisted into a ponytail at my neck. I'm not sure why, but when I saw it, it made me want to cry.

And sure enough, once the initial brouhaha that followed my escape died down, things went rather better. I did go over to his house now and then, on special occasions. Three or four times a month we'd meet up for lunch or for dinner or a coffee. I even enjoyed it. When it was just the two of us, things were different – as they always had been. He didn't feel the need to put on an act. He didn't bluster, he didn't act the clown, he didn't pontificate. We went for walks and we chatted. We went for an ice-cream. I described the books I was reading or the courses I was doing at university. I teased him constantly and, laughing, he let me. At worst he said, 'You're very mean,' which was very true. Things between us were cautiously rudimentary, but that was OK. Life with those we have loved is chiefly made up of superfluous words and silences, isn't it, looking back? For the first time in a long time I was catching glimpses of what seemed to be his truest nature; a sort of covert tenderness; the joy in doing things together. For the first time in a long time I was capable of feeling affection for him.

It wasn't always easy. The masks he wore, the inane jokes, the cheap digs he couldn't help making at me when he had an audience or was in a situation he found uncomfortable, all continued to upset me to what, even at the time, I realised was an excessive degree. There were times when he blithely persisted in needling me and I flew into a rage again, and felt the old despair, the same old crippling shame.

He gave me driving lessons up in the hills at Sassi, in mysterious neighbourhoods I'd never frequented, up beyond the monumental cemetery, in my mother's car – which she lent us with understandable trepidation.

He didn't talk about himself much. I had found out from my mother, in whom he occasionally confided, that he had numerous worries because the cooperative he worked for was in serious financial trouble, and there were other personal sorrows – the usual disappointments over people he had trusted. He never told me any of this himself. But his face was increasingly vulnerable, wounded.

Once, when I was about twenty, for some demented reason I wrote him a letter and posted it. I don't remember exactly what I wrote. A gesture of reconciliation of some sort, I think, although perhaps not explicitly. The one thing I do remember about it is that, in a fit of melodrama, I thanked him for having recognised me, legally, as his child and for having accepted his role as my father. He was overcome. He replied with a heartfelt letter saying that he hadn't recognised me just because he felt obliged to: that I had been wanted, even if he hadn't realised beforehand that that was what he wanted. That he was happy and proud to have me as a daughter. That he wouldn't have changed me for anything or anyone in the world. He also wrote – and I don't remember if this was in the same letter or another one (like all sentimental people, he was very prolific from an epistolary point of view) – that our getting closer again had been wonderful, and that he loved the conversations we had, that sometimes they gave him 'pointers' for his own life. Subsequently, he would, from time to time, bring up the story of my letter (to be fair, it was the only letter I ever wrote him, apart from Christmas and birthday cards), and got emotional about it. I always changed the subject.

I will never stop asking myself how things could have gone if we'd had more time. If we hadn't wasted all those years.

And then it all came to an end in the worst of all possible ways.

I want to try to pin down something of what he was. The things he was.

He had a superhuman memory (which, in hindsight, turned out to be a cruel irony). For example, he still remembered dozens of the poems he had studied at school, word for word, and every now and then he would suddenly recite a random verse, almost as though it were an oral automatism, letting the words flow over his tongue for the pure pleasure of their sound. He only had to read something once to remember it all, or almost all of it, astonishingly accurately. There was a game we used to play: one of the two of us would give the other a clue about a film – the name of one of the lead actors, or a supporting actor, or the subject matter, or the director, or the year it came out, or the title. And the other player had to name the director and cast, or at least the leads. He remembered *everything*, from Cukor to Euro-crime films starring Tomas Milian.

He knew whole cantos from the *Divine Comedy* off by heart. Or rather, cantos from the *Inferno*. He said there were fewer marvels in *Purgatory* and that *Paradise* was just dull propaganda. Whenever he recited Dante he lit up, as though he'd only discovered it the night before. 'Woe to you, perverted souls!' he wauled, radiantly, and always in the same booming voice, flapping his hands in the air. And as for his version of, 'The devil, Charon, with eyes of glowing coals,' well, I don't reckon I'll ever hear its like again. Paraphrasing Farinata degli Uberti, he always said I liked proclaiming my disdain for all this hell, and he would phone me up and ask, laughingly, 'So, are you still proclaiming your disdain?' And the other bits he loved reciting were Ugolino, Paolo and Francesca and Ulysses. Their misadventures and the harrowing repetition of their punishments made him quite emotional. When, as a teenager, I decided off my own bat to learn a few sections, he was thrilled. It was our one and only sacred text, apart from the Greek myths of my childhood. And even now, if I ever find myself quoting Dante to some poor undeserving soul, I hear his cadences in my voice, the extravagant emphases for which there was no particular rationale apart from his enthusiasm.

As he got older he became increasingly cantankerous, but he never lost his gift for finding pleasure in things, in his own feverish way. He had a talent for joy.

He read almost only essays. Mostly, for obvious reasons, on psychoanalysis. (In the last few years of his life he wielded the word 'archetype' like a cudgel.) I once asked him what his favourite novel was, assuming he had one. Without a second's hesitation, he answered, '*Memoirs of Hadrian*, I think. It's one of the loveliest things I've ever read.' I was amazed: a book about old age, about death ... He, of all people, who stubbornly refused to contemplate either of them.

But there was at least one other novel he loved. It was *Wildcat Under Glass* by Alki Zei. I remember the cover of his battered old copy of the Einaudi edition, which I found very disturbing: there was a painting of a tiger skin, or a stuffed tiger, left abandoned on a chair, its slack-jawed mouth turned at a three-quarter angle towards the viewer, its blank-eyed stare lost in the distance. I read it when I was very little, back in the days of the attic (but I'm pretty sure it came from my mother's house and he had taken it away with him: so, finally, there was something he had remembered not to leave behind), and I understood almost none of it. The backdrop to the story was the birth of the Metaxas dictatorship in Greece in the summer of 1936 – I think the only thing I really took away with me was the suffocating sense of danger that descended on the family at the centre of the story. I do, however, remember the two little girls who were its protagonists: two sisters, one called Melissa and the other called Myrto. Myrto was the more argumentative of the two, more impertinent, more interesting. My father like Myrto too. He told me he'd wanted to call me Myrto but my mother (thank goodness) had refused. That book is another thing that has vanished off the face of the earth.

I don't know anything else about his life as a reader, but every now and then he would surprise me. One example: I was fifteen and was reading *Lolita* for the first time. Chosen entirely at random, although even as I read it I did, very confusedly, sense that this was a major event. I was finding it hard to come to terms with the idea of the untrustworthy narrator, and I couldn't work out whether or not I should believe Humbert Humbert when he recounted his version of the death of Dolores's mother. We were on the beach and my father was sitting next to me, reading a newspaper. I propped myself up on my elbows and asked, 'Have you read this?'

'Yes.'

'But Humbert ... he didn't kill his wife, did he?'

He smiled slyly.

'*Of course* he killed her,' he said. He looked back down at his newspaper, and then a little bit later he added, 'You shouldn't believe anything he says.'

Nine years later, when I began to read my way through all of Nabokov, informed enough to understand what I was reading, I finally saw how precious that brief remembered episode had been – a first inkling that in my father there was perhaps something more interesting, more enigmatic and more complex than I had imagined; that I had known almost nothing of his mind, of his real mind. But I never got to talk to him about it: I read *Lectures on Literature* and *Pale Fire* two months after he died. I was never able to talk to him about how I find Pnin so strangely heartbreaking, and about the nutcracker that falls into the sink, and the anecdote about the death of Alexander Chernyshevsky in *The Gift* and the fictitious French philosopher Delalande who, 'asked at someone's funeral why he did not bare his head (*ne se découvre pas*), replied: "Let death unveil herself first" (*qu'elle se découvre la première*).' And Chernyshevsky, who remarked: 'In that gesture there is a metaphysical lack of gallantry, although death surely deserves nothing better.' But the memory of that little episode remains especially precious. Like a shared secret.

The last book I ever lent him was *Life and Fate* by Vasily Grossman, because of certain rather difficult conversations we had had about Soviet communism. He read it in hospital. He couldn't help boasting to the man in the bed next to his – a teacher – that his daughter had lent it to him. He told me, beaming, that the other man had been impressed and had said, 'You must be very proud.' He even managed to finish it, slowly. I only got that book back four years later, when I went back to Dora's house for the first time after his death. That night, in bed, I looked for the apparently arbitrary pencil underlinings that he inflicted on everything I ever lent him, including my dissertation. At first glance there weren't any. I flicked through the pages with growing anguish. But no, there they were: only three of them, though. Not the dozens I would have expected. One was a sarcastic reference to the tears shed by the Kapo and *Blockältester* in a German concentration camp. The second was a phrase which I suspect he had found rather lovely and curious, describing an old man: 'The fusing of the blue of his skin and the blue of his eyes.' The last one was much further on, towards the end of the book, when the mother-in-law of a man who has lost everything kisses his head while he stares speechlessly at the walls of the house he has to abandon. 'This is nothing, my dear, it's nothing. It's just life.'

He was always singing. As I think I've already said, he was rather noisy. He even sang in the street, and I would elbow him and hiss, 'Dad, please don't.'

When he sang in the car he waved his arms around like a windmill, emphasising certain lines of the song with grandiose gestures and yelping: 'Did you get that? "The enormous raspberry ice-cream factories slowly smoking"! That's *poetry*, that is!'

'If you don't keep your hands on the wheel, we'll crash, and that wouldn't be very poetic,' I answered, drily.

But actually, most of the time I sang along with him, equally out of tune and gesticulating equally wildly. Our finest interpretation was reserved for 'Carlo Martello torna dalla battaglia di Poitiers'. Here follows a random and partial list of songs yelled out over the course of approximately twenty years' worth of car journeys made together, long and short: 'L'auto targata "TO" ', 'Il testament', 'Brennero '66', 'Proposta' and 'Tema' (my innumerable pointless talents include perfect imitations of the voices of all the members of the Giganti), 'Canzone di notte', 'Alice', 'I treni per Reggio Calabria', 'Ballata per Ciriaco Saldutto', 'L'abbigliamento di un fuochista', 'Contessa', 'Nel cuore, nell'anima', 'Coda di lupo', 'Berta filava', 'Noi non ci saremo' (the Nomadi version; 'Augusto!' my father invariably wailed, whenever he heard Daolio's voice. As we have already seen with regard to Palinurus, he was steadfast in his pitying), '4 marzo 1943', 'Sognando la California', 'Il feroce monarchico Bava' ('*tu non riiider, sabauda marrrmaglia*'), 'Pezzi di vetro', 'Dio è morto', 'Il signor Hood', 'Singapore', 'Per i morti di Reggio Emilia', 'Bartali', 'Escluso il cane', 'Il mio canto libero', 'La locomotiva', 'Pablo', 'Ho visto un re', 'Tammurriata nera' (in this case, the sounds I emitted were mostly fragmentary yelps, because I didn't understand a word of the dialect, but adored it anyway),

'Stalingrado' and 'La fabbrica', 'Ma come fanno I marinai'. There were cassettes with compilations of 1950s rock 'n' roll – although he only sang the choruses or hummed along, tapping his fingers on the steering wheel, because he didn't understand the English: 'Why Do Fools Fall in Love', 'Oh, Carol', 'La Bamba', 'See You Later Alligator', 'Tutti Frutti', 'Let's Twist Again', 'That'll Be the Day', 'Only You', 'Under the Boardwalk', 'Summertime Blues', and so on and so forth. 'Rimini'. 'Il leone e la gallina', 'Generale', 'Disperato erotico stomp', 'Pugni chiusi' ('*in me c'è la noo-tte più neeeraaa*' – inside I'm bla-ha-haack as niiight: which had to be voiced with an American-style gulp), 'Lugano addio', 'Il vestito di Rossini', 'Sant'Antonio a lu desertu', 'Bufalo Bill', 'Vengo anche io (no tu no)', 'Porta Romana bella', '29 settembre', 'Santa Lucia', 'Acqua azzurra, acqua chiara', 'Un altro giorno è andato', 'Fila la lana', 'Ballata per Franco Serantini', 'Rimmel', 'Ahi, Maria'. Etc., etc.

If our family has any sort of archive, this – I think – is it. An ephemeral, inane, impalpable archive the unique and unrepeatable gist of which – life – can't be described without the words landing wildly off target. 'How poor is the language of happiness!'

Someone (someone who had nonetheless loved him very much) once said to me (and said it with genuine pity): 'It can't have been easy having him as a father.'

No, it hadn't been. It hadn't been right to the bitter end. And it hadn't been easy, afterwards, to listen to all those strangers telling me what a wonderful father he must have been. I limited myself to smiling politely.

I had felt I knew him. I knew the darkest, cruellest, cheapest nooks and crannies of him. And I knew him in his moments of limpid grace. I had thought I'd understood him in his entirety. But now I had to acknowledge that I didn't know him as well as I'd thought. That perhaps I hadn't known him at all.

It was practically impossible even to begin to piece together his life story, even in broad intervals. He had never told me anything about his childhood, about his mother and his father, about his brothers and sisters as children. Much less about himself. I had no idea whether it was out of indifference or a deliberate erasure. There was just a lone pair of often-repeated anecdotes about a funny great-aunt who died a long time before I was born, his *zia*, his auntie, Ziella. Zia Ziella. (As a little girl, I hadn't understood that Ziella was a diminutive of Graziella, and I thought 'Zia Ziella' must be a conventional formula of some sort, like in Homer. An uber-aunt, let's say.) And then his brothers and sisters all died in the space of four years, just before and just after he did, beginning with the youngest and finishing with the eldest. There was no one left to ask. I knew he'd been born in Monte Sant'Angelo, at the top of a mountain, in the final December of the war, and that twelve years later the family had returned to Trani, on the coast. I struggled even to remember the names of his parents. As for whoever came before them, their names are buried in total oblivion. But this is equally true in my mother's case, and she told me a great deal about her childhood self, about her brother and her parents, about her father who told stories in the cowshed on winter evenings when the whole village gathered to gossip and keep warm (or to shell the corn), and about her mother who had been in service from the age of eight until she married. But she had never been able to tell me much about even her grandparents, except that they were peasants.

My mother had one day confessed that she always felt a terrible, almost shameful envy when she read those autobiographies of writers who came from aristocratic or upper-middle-class families with family trees going back to the Ice Age, and who possessed, scattered across the centuries and recorded in family chronicles, a multitude of fascinating ancestors with a history of eccentric habits, heroic deeds and rash marriages, or simply an elegant profile and porcelain skin immortalised in honeyed verse by some contemporary amateur poet.

'I have ancestor envy,' she said, half joking, half not.

I could see what she meant. We didn't have any ancestors. We have no idea who our forebears were. And for one very simple reason: they were poor and illiterate, so they've left no trace. No trace in the north of Italy and no trace in the south. That old expression, 'Who do you take me for? The maidservant's child?' (which even I have heard myself use), was one she particularly disliked. And in effect, she *was* the maidservant's child. We are descended from servants, from that anonymous multitude who formed a mute backdrop, never more than functional or decorative in scope, to the scenes in other people's novels and autobiographies. What my mother envied was that culture they acquired even before birth, their inherited libraries, the illustrious contacts and teachers, the ease of access, the riches handed down – and I don't mean monetary.

Sometimes I felt that envy too.

I have honestly never been all that interested in the idea of lineage or in 'roots' and all those allusions to identity and origins. It's stuff I instinctively avoid. My loyalties, if that's what you could call them, are of a different kind. But if I stop to think about all those individual fates and the fact that they have been so completely obliterated by the passing of time, I find it quite upsetting. How I'd love to have a mad clairvoyant ancestress or a great-grand-father who took potshots at the ornaments on the mantelpiece! And instead, of all those people who preceded me, not a trace remains; I'm not saying there should have been traces of their sentiments or their desires or of some fleeting thought that once occurred to one of them on the edge of sleep, but there wasn't even an anecdote handed down from generation to generation, or an obvious family trait.

A few months ago, the widow of one of my great-uncles died – he was one of my maternal grandmother's brothers. She was called Venilia. When it happened, someone told me that she had been a 'maidservant's child' too. Her mother had been a young housemaid in some rich man's house when she had fallen pregnant. I spent a long time thinking about that serving girl who'd chosen such a pretty and unusual name for her daughter. I wondered if she'd read it somewhere, if she could read, or if she had heard it said in passing, or if she had remembered it from some story she had been told as a child and was particularly fond of. That young girl, alone and poor, who had wanted to give her fatherless baby a special name. Wanting her, perhaps, to have something unique, something that was hers and hers alone.

An individual who left a trace: a girl, one day in the 1920s, who chose a name.

Apropos of legacies. Whether it was during that first meeting or months later, I don't remember, but at some point Agata told me she had always wondered what happened to the pocket watch her father had given my father when they got married; it was a family heirloom that her father had inherited from his father, etc. She would have wanted me to have it (not her own children: me, because I was Leonardo's daughter), but it had been lost in who knows which house move. Me, the female child, inheriting the object that had always symbolised the handover from one generation of men to the next, to a new family. It would have been curious. But my father had never been any good at looking after things, even when they were important to other people.

So, his childhood wasn't available. I had only an imagined idea of the place he was born: a village of snow-white houses on a mountainside, dominated by the fifteen-century-old shrine erected on top of a grotto back when the region belonged to the Lombard kings, and by the crumbling towers of the Norman castle which had been a state prison under the Angevins. Up where – I read – the wind scoured the roads all year round, and a thick and lingering fog descended every autumn. I tried to imagine the little boy: I caught glimpses of his little outline turning round to look at me in one of those steep village lanes, in the fog; but I couldn't see his face.

And Rome. Rome was equally ghostly. What had he done there? Who had he been? There was no one I could ask. Although, actually. There had been – I remembered – a time, one summer, when we had walked past a poster for a film (having checked the dates, I'd guess I was twelve) and, as nonchalantly as if he were remarking on the weather, he had said, 'You know, I shared a flat with that director for a while, when I lived in Rome.' And we walked on. I had asked Agata about it and she told me it was true: at some undefined point in the 1960s, my father had lived in the same house as the film director and the Swedish actor who often worked with him back then. When I later read that both of them – director and actor – had been in Serve the People, it wasn't hard to guess how their paths had crossed. I have never had any contact with either of them. Although, to begin with, I did try, because it was the only feeble link I had, the only hope of knowing something about that piece of his life. But there were too many complications, and in the end I gave up. One day, perhaps.

Later on, Agata also told me about a girl my father had gone out with in Rome, but Agata only knew her Christian name, Clara, and that she came from a rich family. When the family had found out who she was seeing, they had grounded her, and my father had gone round there and had staged a vaudevillian solitary protest in their courtyard, complete with megaphone and banner demanding that they 'Free Her'. The stunt, it seems, was so effective that, dying of embarrassment, they let her out immediately, and love triumphed over the bourgeoisie. But Agata had no idea what had happened to Clara, who, as far as she was concerned, had only ever existed in my father's stories; and she definitely didn't know her surname. So Clara, too, remained relegated to the rank of ghost. Because of her Germanic name, I envisaged her having Teutonic hair, straw-blond, long and silky;

and for some reason I always ended up picturing her in clothes from the early 1900s, like a Proustian maiden on the beach in Balbec. Clara *disparue*.

I took it for granted that, in Rome, my slippery protagonist – who, I began to realise, now lived an autonomous existence in my head, entirely detached from that of the man I had known (and whom from now on we will call L.B.) – had participated in the assemblies and then the occupations in the autumn and winter of 1967–1968, perhaps at the Faculty of Medicine, or at the Faculty of Literature, or Architecture, or all of them, or some. The one thing I do know is that he once told me that 'when we occupied' they had to study twice as hard, because they had to teach their own courses in lieu of the lecturers, so that they would be able to sit their exams. He was profoundly offended by any suggestion that the students had occupied the universities because they didn't want to study. To him, study was sacred; it was the fundamental point of his life on earth. I took it for granted that he went along – to the assemblies and the occupations – because he thought it was his duty and (knowing what he was like) perhaps even a moral imperative. Perhaps he was thinking of the kids from the deprived suburbs whom he'd helped at the after-school club, and asking himself what future awaited them, and whether this might not be a way of offering them a chance to circumvent predestination and escape the ancient and iron-clad solitude in which they were immured. And then, it must have been so liberating, so incredibly *new*, coming together with other people like that. The feeling of justice being done, the thrill of the adventure, the vague but mighty sensation of an epoch dawning. All those words flowing endlessly. All that youth.

He was twenty-two. With the arrogance of a twenty-two-year-old, he must have thought he already knew almost everything he needed to know, and that the rest would come to him along with all those words which seemed so perfect and which seemed to dissolve and to govern the mystery of the world. He must have thought he was immortal, unbreakable, complete. That time had ceased to exist.

I looked everywhere for him. For weeks and weeks I studied dozens and dozens of photographs and films, the wounded being dragged away by their arms at Valle Giulia, the burnt-out police vans, the shadows running through columns of smoke, the silhouettes clambering up grassy banks or running down them, the group photos taken during marches or assemblies, which I zoomed in on, enlarging the images to the maximum size possible, and scanning them for hours on end in the hope of finding him; the grainy film clips of 16 March, the day the neo-fascists made their punitive incursion and the desks were thrown out of the windows: the same day on which, on the other side of the world (but this would only become public knowledge much later on), Lieut. William Calley's soldiers were killing and throwing out into the street, and into the wells and into the ditches, thirty-eight of My Lai's old women and children and newborn babies, and setting fire to their homes.

I never did catch sight of him: it was all too fast, too age-worn, too far away. I don't know why I was so obsessed, but I *needed* to see him there. If I couldn't know anything about that fragment of his existence, I wanted at least to see him. He had been part of an historical event. But he was never there. It was unbearable. Could it be that, not knowing what he had looked like back then, I simply hadn't recognised him? I even dreamed I found a black-and-white film clip in which he was running along at the edge of a protest march, recognisable, happy, a young man, like one of those joyful scenes in *Heimat*. There he was, L.B., immortalised in time: in my dream I smiled triumphantly, finally placated.

Legend has it that on the shores of Lake Svetloyar, lost amid the forests of Nizhny Novgorod to the north of the Volga, the fabled city of Kitezh was once to be found. When, following a traitor who led them along a secret trail, the Tatars arrived to conquer the city, the city sank into the lake, slowly vanishing right before the invaders' astonished eyes. The last thing to have shone out across the water, before sinking along with everything else, was the church's golden dome. For ten days and ten nights the Tatars searched for it in vain.

It is also said that Kitezh is still there, beneath the water, secretly alive, with all its inhabitants. And, say the Old Believers' latter-day chronicles, lucky wayfarers occasionally still glimpse its white-and-gold outlines beneath the surface of the lake, and hear the muffled chiming of its bells.

Those were strange months. I continued doing all the usual things: I read, for work; I let opportunities slip through my fingers; I went for walks with N. on Sundays and watched films with him, or read things I liked to him in the park or on the sofa in my small flat. In March we went to Paris and stayed with S., my best friend throughout our adolescence and twenties: we had shared a desk one year at high school, and had watched dozens of art-house films in near-empty cinemas where it was usually just us and two or three nutters, and then there had been a series of adventurous and wonderful holidays. She had been in Paris for a couple of years by now, doing a PhD in chemistry and living with the French boyfriend she would eventually marry. S. was the practical one of the two of us and her pragmatism intimidated me at times, the almost military determination with which she accomplished everything she set out to do. She had been party to my most secret thoughts, had listened to the saddest and most terrible confessions I made to anyone before N. appeared in my life. It was she who accompanied me to my father's wedding, seven days before he died – the last time I saw him alive – and he was very happy to see her there, because he was fond of her. For the whole of that awful afternoon S. had watched over me protectively, in the middle of all those strangers, and her watchful green gaze was all that kept me from liquefying. It was she who took me out for supper the day my father died, and listened to me coldly describing the day's events (the only time I cried was when I got to the bit about the gauze on his eyes), and then we hung around for a while, talking, in the park on the other side of the river, sitting on the grass in the airless night. I had told her that it actually wasn't that big a deal, that a twenty-four-year-old can't really complain about being half-orphaned, that people survive much greater losses. The usual guff. And I really believed it. I said it would have been a thousand times worse had it been my mother – the mere thought took my breath away. S. said nothing. We could see the brightly lit piazza on the other side of the river. Then she walked me home. Before we got to the door of my building, I remember her stopping underneath the scaffolding on one of the neighbouring apartment blocks, and saying gently, 'You're the first,' meaning the first of our group of friends and acquaintances to have lost a parent. 'It puts you in a different place. You've crossed a line, whether you like it or not. And one of these days you're going to have to deal with it.'

During the one moment we had to ourselves that week in Paris, one evening after supper, I told her what I'd found out, and about the plans forming unexpectedly in my head. As I spoke, she listened carefully, looking down at her hands, which were resting, clasped together, on the table. Then she lifted her grave feline face and looked straight at me and said, bluntly, unsentimentally, unperturbed, just the way I needed her to be: 'Do it.'

During that week in Paris I also met up with Valérie Z., a French-Israeli writer who lived in the Marais and whom I'd known for several years. We had met in 2009 at a book festival – I was presenting a children's novel she'd written – and had found one another delightful. Valérie was an enchanting creature, with huge long-lashed black eyes and very short blue-black hair which she decorated with circlets of flowers. She had an irresistible laugh, and we had chatted, in French, for hours, sitting on a stone bench, and again that evening at supper: she was one of those people you find yourself confiding in instinctively within minutes of first speaking to them. And her own story was fascinating: born in Nice to a Jewish family, she had been taken to Israel as a teenager when her parents decided to move there, and she had had to deal with all the implications of that extraordinary uprooting, including military service; then, as an adult, she had chosen to move back to France.

I had seen her again two years after that, at another literary festival, in Sardinia. That was just a fortnight after my father's death, but I had decided to go all the same. I was there to promote my second children's book, which had come out a month and a half earlier: when it was presented at the *Salone del Libro* in Turin, my father had come along, despite being heartbreakingly ill. And I had seen how other people looked at him, startled, or avoided looking at him. He had come along, despite being barely able to sit upright, and had coughed continually, and every now and then had dozed off and Dora had had to wake him, gently squeezing his arm (my mother told me later).

At the festival in Sardinia I wandered around utterly detached, surrounded by people, noise and constant questions, and trailed by the ten-year-old daughter of one of the organisers. As little girls often do with young women, she had chosen me as her favourite. I was perfectly happy to chat to her, but seemed to be looking at her and listening to her from inside an aquarium. For the first and only time in my life, I had asked my mother to accompany me to a festival: I couldn't have handled it otherwise. I was going through a phase of not wanting to be photographed, but she insisted, one evening, after we had got ourselves dressed up for the final dinner. In that photograph I see a person I have difficulty recognising, with a strangely blank face, unreadable eyes, the hint of a tight smile, hair in a plait wound around my head (I often wore it that way at the time), hands twisted together in my lap, and a flowery cotton dress that left my shoulders bare. That was the dinner at which, unexpectedly, I saw Valérie again: I hadn't noticed her name in the programme, but then again, I had only run a cursory eye over it. We embraced, happily, and she sat next to me at the table and we resumed talking as though our conversation had only broken off a few minutes earlier.

'*Qu'est-ce qu'il y a, Marta?*' she asked me after a while, in – to my great surprise – a very serious tone; and there was I, thinking I'd been so successful at keeping my feelings hidden. I'd been doing nothing but that, for weeks, for months. For years.

'*Il y a deux semaines, mon père est mort,*' I replied simply. Those kind eyes of hers widened, and she stared off into the distance and said how sorry she was, placing one of her hands on mine. I said something similar to what I'd said to S. that evening by the river, but in a slightly sugar-coated version. Valérie said many things to me during that dinner, hoping to make me feel better, I think; but I forget exactly what (in my defence, I had had a lot of Sardinian wine).

And there we now were, in a *pâtisserie* in Places des Vosges, one of those places so full of gold and mirrors and beautiful crystal that I felt almost embarrassed to be there. She told me she was writing (or perhaps she'd just finished it) a novel about a young uncle of hers who had died in the war, Jacob, who had been a member of the Jewish community who were driven out of Algeria following independence, and that it had all been inspired by a photograph, which she showed me. And I told her that I was digging up stuff about my father and finding it much more interesting than I could ever have imagined. She was enthusiastic.

'Oh God,' I said, frustrated, having searched in vain for the right word for a particular concept, 'isn't it terrible when you can't say what you want to, even when you speak a language quite well. I feel ... thick. It feels like you only know a reduced version of me, a thicker version.'

'Oh,' she said gently, 'I know just how you feel. You can't imagine how well I know how you feel. When we moved to Israel, I knew maybe five words of Hebrew. And I stopped talking. No one knew anything about me because I didn't know how to tell them. And everything I'd ever been up to that point, all my complexity ... it all vanished. The precision of an adjective, the nuances, my irony, everything that makes up your personality, *n'est-ce pas*? I'd become a sort of vague outline. Eventually, I picked it up and that feeling passed, but I certainly haven't forgotten what it's like.'

Later, before we said goodbye, we stopped for a minute in the square. After days of rain and drizzle, we finally had a day of good weather. I scanned the square, looking for the sandpit in front of which, when I was eighteen, together with S. and G. – another friend of ours whom I'd known since we were at primary school – we'd sat down on a bench to have a rest, and had spent over an hour watching the toddlers play. There were girls lying on the grass, reading and eating cakes in the sun. Valérie suddenly said, as though picking up the same conversation, 'One could argue that we spend our whole lives translating what we're trying to say into what we actually manage to say.'

Spring dragged on and I met up with people and I met new people and I went to literary events, sometimes, in the evening. And I worried about the bills, I worried about the rent, I worried in general, and I read the news, aghast, or finding it all inane. The world had expanded out of all proportion. But that very fact (of being able to know everything, or almost everything, in almost real time, from the remotest of regions or from just around the corner, from earthquakes to torture, people drowning at sea trying to reach Europe, the persecution of peoples I hadn't even known existed, terrorist attacks on every continent) simply increased my sense of impotence.

I came down with continual colds. I had friends from other cities to stay. I taught workshops for schoolchildren. I collaborated on frustrating projects for which I was badly paid or not paid at all. I got angry with myself and then let it drop, because I always let it drop. I let everything that happened wash over me as though I were asleep or in a trance, but I never slept properly. I carried on doing all of this, and on the face of it I hadn't changed at all; but all the while, I was ... What's the best way to put this? Haunted, I suppose. I was haunted, and this thing that possessed me made me feel daring, it made me feel charmed, as though I were being swept forward by it. Even the way my body moved through space was more rapacious than usual.

It was as though an underground existence rolled on in parallel with the visible world: me waiting for the next meeting with someone who would describe another fragment of L.B. to me; the slow, patient search for names, faces or circumstances in the documents, the books, the newspaper archives; and the emotion in the voices on the phone, and in the voices of all the strangers I was gradually put in touch with. That shook me, every time. Although decades had passed, and although they hadn't seen him after that ('apart from that time we walked past him in the street'), it seemed that the mere idea of spending an hour or so remembering him – and remembering what they themselves had been, so many years ago – filled them with a warmth which surprised me each and every time, and filled me, in turn, with an overwhelming tenderness for them. And for the ghost who haunted them all.

It was May, I think. One day, abruptly and almost angrily, I sat down and wrote the piece about the young man running through the night covered in blood, and I began drafting the chapter on my father's death and all the things I knew about him. I wrote for three hours without pausing, with a dull thunder roaring in my ears. With the exception of my dissertation, it was the first time I had written more than a page in over four years. The sensation was half exhilaration and half terror; with that act – and the decision it represented – it felt like I was betraying the un-writable novel I had spent so much time envisaging. And its protagonist. I was killing it off definitively. It also felt like an act of surrender. And what if I really were to make a start on *this* thing ... Oh God. It was going to be so hard, it was going to take so much work, it would take so long just to get it to resemble even a pale shadow of the shimmering torrent coursing through me, and still swelling, and still destined to swell for years to come. But that hunter's instinct was one I recognised well, and it was stirring after a good long sleep. *On ne choisit pas son sujet*, wrote Flaubert, in 1861, in a letter to Madame Roger des Genettes. When I first read that I thought it was a ridiculous thing to say.

I didn't yet know what shape it would take, but the idea was assembling itself in front of me, like an unfinished bridge hanging in the air. And it was thrilling and frightening. The following day I wrote some more. Reluctantly, I had to say something about myself: I was, unavoidably, the narrator. I wrote that my life had been ordinary and void of momentous events; I quoted Mandelstam when he said that a *raznochinets* – one of those petty-bourgeois intellectuals with no past and no money behind them – 'needs no personal history, he has simply to speak of the books he has read and his biography writes itself'. Fundamentally, I thought, that was true: there wasn't much else in the way of substance or direction driving the dull story of my life as a Western *raznochinets* born at the end of the twentieth century into a world of peace and comfort and affection and cultural opportunities. I wrote that my 'real' life wasn't interesting. I had never found it interesting. When I was a little girl, I had made a start on several diaries but always abandoned them out of boredom a few days later: there was nothing to say. I had always preferred making things up.

Even when it came to my relationship with my father, I was perfunctory and covered it briskly, in a couple of pages. The story I cared about wasn't that one. It was the other one. I was satisfied: I'd eliminated myself. I had made matters clear.

Now all I had to do was to carry on collating those other people's voices, and decide what to do with them.

A few days later another isolated recollection came to me: my father, in my mother's flat, halfway through a conversation I've long forgotten, smiling hesitantly and giving me a sideways look and saying, 'One day you'll write a book about your father.'

I had snorted.

'You must be joking.'

He had roped me into doing it, in the end.

The novelist was thin and spare, his frame deceptively slight: it gave the impression his bones might be hollow, like those of a bird. And even the long, thin nose with its arcuate tip had something avian to it, like a heron. His cheekbones were visible beneath that thin, lightly tanned skin. He wore round spectacles, a sharp white beard and had rather deep-set eyes with heavy lids, giving him an air that seemed weary and penetrating (weary, but also penetrating). He was polite and sad; the sadness he exuded seemed immense, ineluctable, far too big for his slender body. We were sitting at a little table under the porticoes inside the Rotonda della Besana on a sunny day, and there was hardly anyone else around. He was talking, in that low, kind voice of his. I was wearing a blue dress and taking notes which I would later lose in a house move. We'd never met before.

What had happened was this. A couple of months earlier I had been reading an autobiographical novel he'd written. A friend had lent it to me ('Among other things, it talks about his years in Serve the People. You might find it useful,' said my friend). There was one passage in which he was talking to Brandirali and mentioning a school for party cadres which had been organised in a hotel in Boca, in Valsesia, and at a certain point a figure appeared whom I recognised instantly, even before I'd finished the paragraph describing him. A shiver ran through me so hard that my teeth almost chattered. It was C.C., 'that old poseur' with whom Brandirali was 'particularly taken', and he was talking about the struggles of the miners in his hometown and using exactly the words the novelist would find, years later, in one of Zola's novels. C.C., the former miner, who touched up the female militants who didn't dare push him away for fear of 'looking like petty bourgeoisie jealous of their class privilege'. In the dining room, he stood on the table and bellowed, and raised a glass to Brandirali and yelled at him to find him a wife. I knew who C.C. was and I knew how this had all ended. He was the one from the Via Artisti business. And the novelist eventually mentioned the affair, but a few of the details were wrong: he'd probably only heard them second- or third-hand.

But that wasn't important. I needed to speak to him. If he'd known C.C., maybe he'd known my father. I wrote to an editor friend of mine and he got hold of contact details for me. The novelist had agreed to meet me. And so there we were. We had met up in front of what used to be a record shop, at Porta Romana.

I showed him a few photos of my father, hoping he'd recognise him, even though they were fairly recent. But he looked at them and smiled wanly and said, 'I'm not sure. Those years were a bit of a blur, in my case. And also, we covered different areas. We may well have met at some point ... but we all had beards back then.'

He talked about Serve the People in the same way Agata did: like a long sickness. He told me he'd almost always been drunk when he'd been obliged to speak at rallies, because he coped with it better that way. He seemed to have hated every second of it, even when he was still taking part: he didn't seem to have ever, even for a moment, felt he was on a mission which justified the inhuman sacrifices, the need to turn a blind eye to so many things, the self-importance, the cult of the leader, the utilitarian art, the infantile mythologising of Maoist China, the attempts to justify Stalin (which almost all of them, he pointed out, thought were pure fantasy), the intrusion into the most personal, physical aspects of militants' lives. It took me aback. I was taken aback above all by the idea that someone like him could have dedicated so many years of his life to something so anti-artistic, so anti-literary, so dehumanising (human in the sense of the essence of a person, human feelings). And yet he'd hung on – he'd hung on to the bitter end.

'I find it impossible to understand,' was all I said.

His long fingers traced circles on the table.

'It was so easy to end up getting involved at that point – and the same personal history could take you either way. There was a storm brewing, there was something apocalyptic in the air: it felt like it was terribly important to subscribe to something, to be part of something you could fight for, and at the end of the day sometimes it simply boiled down to who got to you first. The Young Fascists, the Young Communists ... if you think about it, the words they used, all the criticisms of capitalism and the bourgeoisie, their intolerance of establishment values and the establishment's rules: sometimes they sounded very similar. And all the while they were propping up the very system they claimed they wanted to destroy, because as long as they kept beating each other up and murdering each other, the people who represented that establishment were left free to carry on doing whatever they wanted.'

Blinking hard, he continued to scrutinise the table.

'It's not that we didn't see it, the absurdity, the stupidity, the more disturbing aspects of it all. But we didn't attach much importance to them. Serve the People had a veneer of intellectualism that no one else apart from the Italian Communist Party had – it seemed more serious, ideologically, than the other extra-parliamentary parties on the far-left, it had a better-defined agenda. There was a palpable need for that. And if they republished Stalin's writings, well, so what! I don't think many people actually read them. Hardly any of us genuinely believed he'd simply made a few errors of judgement and that all the stories were philo-American slander. Although, at the time, we didn't really have any way of knowing *everything* that had gone on in the USSR, and was still going on. Stalin, Mao, Castro ... ultimately, they were mythical creatures, and those lands and all those people were light years remote. We were ignorant, and we chose to be. The truth wasn't particularly important. There was a need for those myths, for a beacon of light.'

He looked back up at me.

'I've known so many people who were destroyed by Serve the People. Who lost everything. Whose talents were destroyed.' He gave me a few examples, but asked me not to name them if I ever wrote about it. 'Some of them killed themselves, afterwards. And others ended up alcoholics or became heroin addicts. It wasn't easy to survive something so all-pervading, so obsessive. No one came out of it intact.'

I didn't say anything. I took no notes.

The novelist asked me: 'Do you want to write about this?'

'I think so. But,' I admitted, 'I still don't know how. There's a whole stack of people I still need to meet. I have to work out how to fit all of this together.'

I found it embarrassing, trying to explain myself. I was worried I'd come across as superficial or presumptuous, when the truth was I was terrified (the familiar combination: fear and desire, desire and fear, the torrent and the shape).

'It's something ... I wasn't expecting,' I concluded vaguely, looking away.

'Well, in that case, please listen to what I'm about to say.' He paused. 'When you come to write about Serve the People ... The world you come from is very different. You view these things with amazement, with irony. And that's understandable. But don't just be mocking. That's too facile. Show these people compassion. They believed in what they were doing and most of them never did any harm to anyone, if not themselves. History ate them alive. Don't deride them too much; don't be sarcastic. Have compassion.'

He still had, he said, a number of booklets and pamphlets produced by Serve the People which he could lend me. He thought they were probably somewhere in his office, which was quite nearby.

'It's important you're familiar with the language they used, if you're to understand,' he explained.

I wasn't entirely sure I wanted to be familiar with the language they used, but I followed him obediently. Once we were upstairs in the little flat he used as an office, the novelist began rummaging around, and he also made a couple of phone calls, because he couldn't remember where he'd stashed the booklets and pamphlets away. In the meantime, I glanced at the books which filled one wall of that calm, white, empty room, in which the only other furniture was a desk near the window and, if I remember rightly, a one-ring hob for making coffee. I liked the things he read, and I found him likeable. A few years later, in one of his collections of essays, I read a delightful parallel drawn between the young Melville, setting sail aboard a whaler, and Emily Dickinson, in more or less the same period ('that other great adventurer'), confined to her small room, and I seemed to recognise something I had vaguely, confusedly perceived when looking at those bookshelves of his.

Eventually the booklets emerged (there were a good dozen of them, with garishly bright covers) and they were handed over to me in a brown paper parcel. I promised to return them intact, sooner or later, and I carried them home tucked under my arm, like a travelling salesman with slightly unorthodox merchandise.

When all was said and done, I began, as time went by, to find it less bizarre that L.B. had joined what was initially known as the *Unione dei Marxisti-Leninisti* – probably when it was founded, in 1968. The student movement wasn't achieving anything practical; there was no programme, there was no clarity any more, either politically or ethically (these are the words used, many years later, by Elia Morgari, another member of the PCIM-L in Turin, and also one of the first friends L.B. made when he arrived in the city). Once the initial enthusiasm had waned, L.B. must have begun to find the dispersive, chaotic character of the movement irritating, and the *Unione* turned up at just the right time. Exactly as the novelist had told me, it gave every impression of incarnating that hunger for orderly process, for organisation, for tangible aims: the field surveys, the concern for peasant farmers and agricultural labourers and not just blue-collar workers in industry, the useful work being done on a day-to-day basis, the ideological apparatus of Maoism which provided a tidy and ready-made explanation for everything and seemed to amortise both the ossification of European socialism and the soviet idea of Socialism in One Country. Hurling 'firecrackers at the La Rinascente department store' wasn't going to solve anything. They wanted to annihilate the system; they found it repugnant: but they wanted to do so methodically. Basically, they just switched churches.

And yet many of them were fairly quick to recognise the nature of the trap closing in on them, and left within the first year or two. So the incomprehensible thing wasn't why he had ever joined. It was why, like the novelist and so many others, he'd hung on right to the bitter end.

And so, one day, L.B. had left for Turin. But when? No one has been able to piece it together with any precision. The most likely hypothesis is that it was 1971.

What is certain is that he went there, and stayed for good. It was Serve the People who sent him. But it is my belief that, in the meantime, something had happened, something which drove him to leave, out of the blue, just when he'd finished all of his exams and was ready to start work on his thesis. There had even been a small article in one of the Roman newspapers in which he was mentioned as a promising forensic medic (he had kept the clipping, which Agata had seen, but then the clipping had disappeared just like everything else). Why would someone like him, with his almost religious veneration for study, have made a choice of that kind?

Unluckily, and like almost all of the truly significant elements in L.B.'s strange story, the answer to this remains lost in the shadowy limbo of piecemeal reports and things badly remembered, with no proof, no dates, no facts. And oddly enough it was Agata who said something to me, *en passant*, years later, while we were waiting for the doors of a lift to open, Agata who said it as though it were an irrelevant detail, a common-or-garden anecdote, and not the one thing that, instead, looking back on it later, would come to me in a flash of perfect clarity as the explanation not for everything but for a great many things in my father's confused and contradictory life: it had been one of those pivotal moments that mark an irreversible fork in a man's road. One of those moments at which he is forced to pick a direction, to choose his fate.

From that passing remark, in other words, I learned that something had disgusted him beyond the limits of the tolerable, something encountered during his oncology internship at a Roman hospital, something to do with the atmosphere of the place, the rank hypocrisy, the self-satisfied vulgarity of it, the servility and brown-nosing, the power games. And it seems he had also heard something about money changing hands in exchange for guaranteed beds for particular patients. The very thing he'd been fighting against for years was what he was about to become. He couldn't bear it, I suppose.

So perhaps he was better off sacrificing his ambitions, if ever he'd really had any, and the pleasure of practising medicine and doing research; perhaps the only concrete way he could make himself useful without making unbearable compromises was to join the faceless masses, to do as the party asked; and to choose that path *in toto* and unreservedly, to fully obey the injunction to make themselves identical to the proletariat they wanted to help, the proletariat they wanted to convince of the fact that a revolution was necessary. A vestigial trace, perhaps, of an earlier Roman Catholic calling to bear witness: going out among the dispossessed, instead of staying behind to lick the boots of senior registrars. Then again, how could he have saved himself while knowing that all those others still out there, all those countless others, would never have access to salvation of any kind? Obliterating oneself, erasing one's own identity – it was an almost obligatory step; as their pamphlets preached, they couldn't afford personal feelings, or they'd lose sight of the greater good, of the ultimate goal: of that vague ideal of happiness for all mankind, which would eliminate every human ill.

We can therefore surmise that this was the point at which it was suggested or decreed he set off for the city where all the factories were. Or rather, the city where the Factory was. He went without telling anyone he was going, not even his family, who heard nothing from him for six months; he simply vanished. After a few weeks without news, his parents telephoned the relatives in Rome who occasionally invited him round for supper: 'Where has Leonardo got to?' And all the relatives could say was, 'We don't know. He left.'

I once had a particularly strange dream: I learned of the existence of a video cassette that my father had recorded, telling the story of his life; he'd left it to Dora, who had organised a screening in somebody's sitting room, and I was in the audience, and it was so hurtful to be sitting in the audience and not to have been the original recipient of the cassette. The video featured tremulous images, originally filmed in Super 8, of a black-and-white mountain landscape which was vast and arid, and which was meant to be where he came from but actually looked more like certain bits of Basilicata or the Gennargentu mountains in Sardinia. Off-screen, my father described the moment of his departure in a voice that was hoarse with emotion: 'All who wish to live must leave the Valley of the Viy.'

I think I've remembered the phrase so precisely because of the slightly odd alliteration, and above all because of the violent incongruity of that image of the Viy, the demon from Ukrainian folklore. But was that really how he felt? *Was* it the 'Valley of the Viy'? Had he really hated that place so intensely, or was it simply my imagination which added the grim bleakness to a sentiment that had been more ambiguous (an awareness of insurmountable differences, but also a frantic tenderness)? I wasn't sure. And what if L.B.'s Viy had been L.B.?

There is a possibility that his arrival in the pivotal city was preceded by an exploratory assignment, because there are people who remember seeing him there in 1969. It may be that there has simply been a degree of confusion with regard to the dates, but it's not all that important.

1969. Casualties in the workplace: an accident every twenty seconds; a life-changing injury every twenty minutes; a death every two hours. 'The numbers sound like a war bulletin,' commented one trade union representative in a film clip from the time. They had had them printed on huge posters which hung at the back of the podium. The posters seemed to throb with those numbers. In Battipaglia – where, 'if you can get them to give you a three-month contract, you've got superpowers', said a weary young man in a group being interviewed in the street; Battipaglia where a sugar-processing plant had just been closed down and the closure of a tobacco factory was on the cards – on 9 April a protest was organised: a klaxon sounded, the baton charges began, the police vans mounted the pavements, bludgeons were used, and when stones were thrown in response, the police fetched machine guns and fired straight into the crowd. (In the same documentary, another tired man points to bullet holes low in the walls – plainly not stray bullets, as the official version had claimed.) Dozens of people were wounded, and two were killed: a young lad, who'd been haunted for months by the images of Jan Palach in flames and that agonising vision of justice; and a woman – a high school teacher who'd been standing on her balcony. A few months earlier the same thing had happened in Avola: a general strike in support of the agricultural labourers' fight to get their collective contract renewed. The police had fired into the crowd. For half an hour. Forty-eight people were wounded and two of the farmworkers died. Two hundred kilos of shell casings were swept up off the street. But it was Battipaglia that finally lit the fuse.

On 11 April 1969 there was a three-hour nationwide general strike in protest at what had happened in Battipaglia. In Turin, at the Factory, where an obsessive discipline reigned alongside efficiency-at-all-costs, where ghostly figures with chronometers glided up and down the assembly line, calculating even the length of time each employee spent in the lavatory, at the Factory where there had been no further protests since the purge of the fifty-five communists who'd gone on strike on 22 January 1953, at the Factory where the rhythms at which they all worked became increasingly inhuman by the day, by the hour, because output was continually surging and in the body shops, where the pace was most exhausting, almost a thousand workers handed in their notice every month, and were immediately replaced by another thousand, in that crystallised realm of perfectly calibrated systems and men who were dutiful, loyal and broken, and who went home in the evening and found to their horror that their hands continued to repeat the gestures of the assembly line in a series of nervous tics, and who saw that assembly line in their nightmares, on 11 April 1969 a strike was called for the first time in fifteen years. The workforce stood back from the machines and walked out en masse, in silence, walking straight past the speechless line managers and security guards.

Thousands of young men, single men, mostly, from the south, had begun arriving in the city many years earlier, coming to work at the Factory. They slept in the train station or in bug-infested rooms that cost them a fortune, or in boarding houses where they paid by the hour and took it in turns to sleep in the beds. When they had wives and children with them, they were piled into cellars and garrets. The city was big, indifferent and cruel: no room was made for them, no one looked out for them. In one book, I read an interview with a man called Salvatore F., who was born in 1940 and came from Potenza down in the south; he had spent nine years at the Factory. The details shocked me. 'The attic they took me to when I first arrived was a filthy hole, and the girl from the Veneto who opened the front door to see who'd turned up told me that the week beforehand it had been occupied by an old man who had hanged himself there. No one knows why. But she showed me the nail he'd knotted his necktie around. It was hard being in Turin all alone. The only time I ever spoke to anyone was at the factory, or when I went to buy food. It felt like they'd cut my tongue out.'

I can picture her, that girl, in slippers and nylon stockings, her hair pulled into a bun at her neck, pointing at the big nail in the ceiling as though it were an exciting curio, a gruesome anecdote to be shared with the lost-looking lad with suitcases piled at his feet. I can picture both of them. I can see every detail.

Lots of them went mad – whatever mad means – and moved straight from the cellars to the lunatic asylum.

Then they packed them off to the outermost suburbs, to

districts created especially for them and their families – whole neighbourhoods of tall buildings swarming with families, in streets prettily named after trees and flowers. The children were, almost all of them, a year or two behind at school, because they only spoke dialect and found the Italian used in the classroom a struggle and were sent back a year, every year, in droves. It was in one of these neighbourhoods that my mother had worked for over two decades, alongside other primary school teachers who had chosen to be *there* in particular, to work with *those* children in particular; and when the children didn't come to school, they went out to fetch them, house by house, waking them up if they'd slept in, bribing, cajoling, trying to explain – mere children themselves, with all the heroic, unbreakable faith children have. There's a school photo from 1973 or 1974, in black and white, in which my mother, who was twenty-three, appears with that elfin face of hers, with her hair in a ponytail, her skull still fully intact (but only for another couple of weeks), wearing a chequered shirt, a white cardigan, bell-bottom jeans; and, with her slender, androgynous body, she doesn't seem much older than the children in her class – all dressed just like her. Almost all of them stand with their arms crossed and with haughty, adult expressions on their faces. Without any hint of a smile.

The eleventh of April marked the beginning. Then there were dozens of other strikes, back to back; there were assemblies identifying specific demands for things which would make working conditions more sustainable and for better-regulated wages; there were regular meetings with the students and with groups of militants outside the factory gates at the end of each shift – encounters in which those two discrete, parallel universes finally succeeded in communicating: the city entered the Factory, and the Factory – the factories – suddenly entered the city. And fierce battles ensued, like the day-long revolt in Corso Traiano on 3 July, when workers from the Factory, students and local residents clashed with the police for fourteen long hours, collecting stones from the still-untarmacked streets, building barricades and hurling flowerpots out of the windows. And then that autumn's protest marches and strikes for the renewal of their collective contracts. Just like the rest of the country. Just like Milan and Genoa and Terni and Porto Marghera and Brescia, and so many other towns and cities. As though something subcutaneous had suddenly erupted, and its flow could no longer be stemmed.

But then the first policeman was killed, at a protest against over-priced rents in Milan, during a baton charge with tear gas and police vans, by a piece of tubing that the protesters had picked up and thrown. And then there was the bomb in the bank, and everything that followed.

One day in the August of 1971, while conducting a search of the office of one of the Factory's clerks who had been sacked without any prior warning and had appealed his dismissal, citing the new Workers' Rights Act which had been passed in response to the campaigns of the previous years (a clerk who, he admitted, had in reality been an incognito company informer), a public prosecutor happened to discover one hundred and fifty thousand dossiers documenting the 'moral character' of the Factory's current and aspiring employees from the late 1940s onwards, dossiers which had been prepared by a vast and extremely efficient network of internal spies.

```
C.C. until recently (December 1949)
played the recorder on Sundays at the
Parish Church of M.C. (ADDENDUM, January
1950: … Impossible to confirm that the
subject did play the recorder at the
Church of M.C., it does however appear
that the entire family, including C.
himself, have communist leanings.)
F.A. (1952): … clerical worker at Fiat
Mirafiori … PCI sympathiser … apparently
heavily pregnant at the time of her
```

wedding … Serious, honest, of average intelligence, well-intentioned. Also arrogant and very uppity. The family all hold moderately extremist [sic] views … fairly unreligious, and in fact on the evening of 31 May 1950, during the procession of the Pilgrim Madonna (happens once a century), they refused to join their neighbours in decorating the building with lights. Has also been heard to mention that her maternal grandfather … had a secular funeral followed by cremation.

<u>C.R.</u> (1957): Has for a number of years had a subscription to the newspaper <u>l'Unità</u>, which he and his family read devotedly.

<u>F.T.</u> (died in Turin 14.04.1960) [this is a dossier on a man who'd been dead for eight months]:

   FAMILY CIRCUMSTANCES: Wife, B.F., is knitting machine operator at small local factory

   FINANCIAL CIRCUMSTANCES: Wife's are straitened

   EMPLOYED: Previously at Fiat Mirafiori as a …, dismissed for political motives approximately five years ago.

   POLITICAL PREVIOUS: Unknown

   DEGREE OF POLITICAL INVOLVEMENT: Unclear

   NORMALLY VOTES: centrist parties:__ right-wing parties:__ left-wing parties: <u>YES</u>

   The deceased was an active communist agitator. Secular funeral, pallbearers were party comrades, coffin carried down to the 'Avvenire' communist club.

PUBLIC REPUTATION: Mediocre
STATE OF HEALTH: Precarious
<u>Recent information regarding family:</u>
POLITICAL INVOLVEMENT: Wife is active
communist agitator, continues to live at
same address and remains domiciled there
REPUTATION: Mediocre
<u>C.G.</u> (October 1962): ... assembly line
worker at Fiat Mirafiori since 1951 ...
Has police record ... some evidence of
communist sympathies given that when the
priest comes round to bless the house
during Easter week he is refused entry
every year.
<u>R.I.</u> (1963): ... PCI sympathiser ...
REPUTATION: Bad, widely reputed to be a
homosexual
Etc.

It was more or less in that period, at some unspecified point in the summer or the autumn, that L.B. arrived in Turin. He may have taken a night train, leaving Rome late in the evening and arriving at the Porta Nuova station at dawn. And in that case, from the window of the train, he must have seen the Piedmont countryside, which would have been all rolling hills to start with and then flatter land for the final pearly hour before sunrise, and damp, silver-green expanses of dew from which, every so often, a farmhouse or a row of poplars emerged. And the landscape would have been empty of men, and the sky would have been vast and still pale, unveiling its brightness slowly, like a curtain rising on the mountains in the distance. Or maybe he had taken a daytime train and arrived in the city at dusk, and had seen those same meadows and fields and hills with the evening light settling on them, yellow and magenta at first, and then a thick royal blue, and blunt banks of fog lifting from the grass, and perhaps a human figure on a path and a dog running on ahead. I wondered what he must have felt as the train pulled into the station, what first glimpse he had that morning (or that dusky evening) of the unfamiliar buildings, as he looked out on to the garden at the centre of the semicircular piazza in front of the station, and the long, straight streets and the porticoes which to me were so intimately familiar. In all honesty, I found it hard to picture him. And equally hard to picture my mother arriving in the city, as she did not long after him. As far as I was concerned they had always been part of this city, and couldn't have belonged anywhere else – as if the city were something they'd inherited, or as if they themselves had begotten it, even; as if it emanated directly from them; and as if, when the moment came at which both of them would eventually have left this world, the city too would somehow, inevitably, cease to exist.

And now L.B. found himself standing at the heart of that city, and perhaps he had the address of a place he was to go to written on a crumpled note in his pocket, and had stopped, for a moment, to get his bearings and to look for a café somewhere close by; and perhaps he felt lost and defenceless, or buzzed with the electrifying sense of this being a fresh start, or perhaps his body shook with all of these things, or maybe he was simply exhausted after the journey. But for an instant, perhaps, for a very brief instant, as he stood there right at the heart of the city, something – a shudder deep in his veins, a presage so fleeting that he didn't even have time to acknowledge it – something perhaps told him that this was where he would remain, that this was the place in which his destiny, whatever that destiny was, would play out. That this was where it would all unfold.

II

LACUNA

It was hard to track L.B.'s movements during those early years in the city. In each of the accounts I was given he flashed up momentarily, with his magical smile, and then promptly vanished. He was there in random fragments: he preached to the crowds outside the university; he took part in a picket; he was out canvassing; he was on a march; he fell in love for a few days; he cooked supper and made a terrible mess of somebody's kitchen; he disappeared for weeks at a time and then reappeared out of the blue; he charmed the socks off a man or a woman he'd just met at the house of some friends, and that man or woman would remember him decades afterwards despite only having spent two hours in his company; he heard some satisfying news and fingered his moustache; he got stopped by the police on a regular basis and immediately released, as reliably and imperturbably as someone clocking off work at the end of a shift.

We don't know where he stayed to start with, if it's true that he arrived in the summer. But for several months, from the November of 1971 onwards, he slept in the hallway of the tiny flat in which Elia Morgari lived with his wife Madruina (although everyone called her Druina). Morgari was twenty-five, a year younger than he was, and, like him, was a member of Serve the People: he was the son of a well-known doctor, the director of the *Istituto di Anatomia e Istologia Patologica*, but the house his parents had bought for him had quickly been made over to the Party, so the flat the young couple lived in was rented, and paid for with Morgari's small party-cadre's stipend. Druina's family was similarly well-to-do, and she, too, was a party militant. Offering comrades somewhere to stay was routine. I met Morgari in the summer of 2016, outside a restaurant up in the hills, where I had arranged to see him together with two other friends of L.B.'s from that period – a couple, Alberto and Lucilla. He and I got there before them. Elia Morgari had a big grey moustache and a face tight with sadness (his wife, his second wife, had been ill for some time). And as soon as he saw me his eyes filled with tears; he squeezed my hand hard and his voice quavered as he said, 'You look like Leonardo,' with the emphasis on the word 'look'; and my face seemed to have shaken him, right to the most vulnerable core of his far-off youth.

People were always telling me that. Even when I was very tiny. And in effect I do look remarkably like him, but a very slightly more feminine version – as he himself used to say with a chuckle. It's only recently, as I've got older, that I've started to look like my mother too. So there was nothing unusual in the phrase. But these people who had seen him when he was younger than I am now, with their incredulous amazement at seeing that much-loved face repeated in mine, so that I became simultaneously myself and a living ghost ... the way these people said it turned it into a form of kindly necromancy, contemporising the past; reversing time and death.

I had heard the same incredulity and the same emphasis on the same word when I met the lawyer who had defended him in the final appeal hearing ('You look so like your father'). He had last seen L.B. in the 1980s, and their relationship had only been formal, but it was the very first thing he said to me.

Morgari had mostly worked out of party headquarters, while L.B. and Druina had been trained up for agitprop – in other words, they took care of propaganda and on-the-ground research, and the hours they spent working for the party were often spent side by side.

From the booklets the novelist had given me, all of them written in the same furiously overwrought and soporific prose (the author, of course, was almost always the party's founder, Brandirali), I had discovered that the work they did, in Serve the People, consisted of paving the way for the imminent revolution by explaining the masses' true will to the masses. The masses were – obviously – intrinsically good, and possessed an innate sense of justice and truth; their will couldn't but be revolutionary, all set to overthrow their masters and oppressors.

Their greatest enemy was pessimism, as I learned from a booklet entitled *Against Idealism* – pessimism being an inevitable by-product of idealism, because, 'insofar as and as long as the material facts are ignored [...] we will continue to encounter a reality which fails to mirror the idealistic vision we set out with, and so, in the end, it is all seen as a failure'. The refulgent dialectic of the booklet's conclusion deserves, I think, to be quoted in full:

> Pessimism cannot but result from feelings which are detached from universal truths. It is a universal truth, for example, that the socialist revolution is destined to prevail in our lifetime. But when reference is made solely to personal feelings and one loses sight of this truth, which is a material truth verified in the collective practice of all mankind, at that point it can be that in the wake of some particular failure, an initiative that has been unsuccessful, or suchlike, we fall prey to pessimism, and lose sight of the universal truth and practically even negate it.
>
> And this individual feeling dares to claim to rival that other feeling which, instead, is a universal truth!
>
> Associated with the second form of idealism, we have the pessimism of those who panic upon seeing that victory is not easy and the battle is arduous, and who conclude that victory is therefore impossible. [...] Instead, we communists look far ahead and see a resplendent future awaiting us, because the true movement advances, overcoming every obstacle, since it is a universal rule that the socialist revolution will prevail worldwide.

There were never any doubts, in that categorical and quixotic version of reality: there was no room for individuals or their contradictions (dismissed as selfish – a waste of time that could be better employed building the revolution), or for life's complexity. And if by any chance any of that complexity ever dared penetrate the chainmail of their faith, the problem was easily resolved by means of self-criticism – or expulsion. They idolised Mankind as an abstract concept, and they wilfully disregarded all of those things which combine to make up a living, breathing man, and all the differences that set one living, breathing man apart from another.

They did also discuss concrete issues – but always and in any event in semi-mystical tones: the right to decent housing, dignified employment, an education; the problem of rents that often ran to more than half a worker's monthly wages; artificially inflated prices; the corruption rampant at every level of government; the bleak financial and cultural poverty in which hundreds of thousands of people still languished; the criminal way in which the south of Italy was being exploited. The party militants were to become the instrument via which the masses would come together, and support the campaigns being waged by the factory workers and farm workers, and unite with them, and fight constantly, within the party itself, to defend the 'proletarian world view'.

The strategy, it seemed, never varied. It was: 'to tirelessly instruct the working masses in communist critique, promoting historical consciousness, a clear vision of the present, a clear vision of the future, so that the working class become the informed protagonists of their own battles. [...] Never losing sight of the importance of the fact that the working class must develop self-understanding.' All of which was to be done, first and foremost, by contributing to the *Servire il Popolo* newspaper, and by distributing it as insistently and widely as possible. Their luminous faith in the masses (whom they saw as a unitary whole, incontestable in its moral splendour, suffocated perhaps by the ugliness amid which it was forced to live, but ready to emerge as if by magic just as soon as it acquired 'self-understanding') was so complete, so ingenuous, and so trusting as to be almost poignant.

'There is no selfishness in the workers' demands. They are capable of loving because they know struggle and toil, they are capable of unity because they know how to organise themselves for productive activities, they are capable of leading because it is they who bring about change in the world. It is within the working class that the wherewithal to lead mankind is to be found: that potent weapon which is altruism.' The masses were good. And they were to make themselves worthy of the masses.

But whatever it was that was supposed to happen *after* the notional revolution remained wrapped in a euphoric fog. The aims of the future revolutionary government's 'programme' were exceptionally vague. Obviously, of course, those who had exploited the working class would be jailed and, should they demonstrate any remorse, re-educated; crèches would be organised in every factory – to help the female workers; the most generous of salaries would never be more than three times the average wages of a factory worker; people's tribunals would be set up; etc., etc. Brandirali wrote that, regardless of the fact that the party's membership only amounted to ten thousand people, they would succeed in convincing the entire nation, petty bourgeoisie included, of the wholesomeness of the project, and of its realism. And in one of the pamphlets I did find a panoramic overview of the future Arcadia, as seen from the celestial balcony of Universal Truth: 'The cities will stretch out harmoniously to merge with the countryside, the hills and the coasts will be inhabited by old folk who gather together at social clubs, and by children and by workers who flock there for rest and recreation. Our land's wine and good food will be produced for everyone: every region will share the best of its products with other regions. The most charming of our popular customs will be resurrected and form part of our collective life. And Italy will be a garden in bloom.'

For a long time, I continued to ask myself whether L.B. had really taken *all* of this seriously. For a long time, I had no idea what he had really thought of the PCIM-L. Until several years later, when I finally met Emanuele Pariante and I encountered a particular typewritten text. But that would be much later on. For the time being I had those booklets to go by, and nothing else, and reading them left me dismayed and irritated; and yet I couldn't help thinking that there must have been times, in the middle of the night, in his temporary home, lying on borrowed sheets, when some doubt, some of that erroneous pessimism which the party condemned, and perhaps even the jolt of a briefly awakened sense of the ridiculous *must* have coursed through him, if only for a moment or two.

But I couldn't be sure. The truth is that even now I have no way of knowing what he thought and felt. All I have is this handful of other people's accounts, emptied of detail by the passing of time, distorted by memory. I have no way of knowing what *he* thought and felt, and that is an irreversible fact. Not just because I can no longer ask him: but because it is simply not possible – and even less possible when the question regards ourselves – to have any inkling of (let alone describe it) the entirety of the life of another person. We barely know anything about ourselves. And even that anything is frequently inaccurate.

He and I were separated by an insuperable distance, and I sensed it even more clearly as he gradually ceased to be just my father and became above all my protagonist, that young man from the past whose face was still only a blur in a very bad newspaper photograph. The young man. How did he feel inside his own skin? Every now and then, quite randomly, I become conscious – in what you could describe as an animal way – of my own hands and legs moving, of the warmth of the sun on one of my shoulders, and other tactile sensations. This is hard to explain: it is as though I were, for an instant, fully aware of (being fully in touch with) my living, breathing body and its movements. And these are the moments when I find it most extraordinary to think that one day I'll die. It's not terror: any fear or denial or refusal of death – my own or other people's – happens at other moments. It is, quite literally, sheer incredulity. How can it be possible that one day I will stop existing? I'm alive. Alive! These eyes are looking at that potted plant on the table on the balcony, these ears are hearing the sough of the wind, this feeling is the caress of the wind on my neck. My living neck. I am, unequivocally, alive. The fraction of a second in which I am alive will last for ever. It cannot be that my body will come to an end; it cannot be that my mind will come to an end.

And now, since I had learned of the existence of that young man, when this thing happened I sometimes found myself wondering what it had been like for him to look and to hear, what it had been like for him to feel time passing in his body, to feel his body occupying space.

I spent three days in Rome for a wedding (I hadn't been back since my one and only visit, ten years earlier, the year I finished high school), and while I was there it often occurred to me. Late in the evening, while N. and his friends and I strolled around Monti and Trastevere, I looked around me and felt secretly separate, as if they and I were on different floors of the same building: so this was what it was like, this was the nocturnal world though which he had moved, fifty years earlier. Fifty years. It sounded so unreal, so enormously far off. And yet he felt remarkably, intensely present, like a blue mist rising from the pavements and encircling me almost constantly, however extraordinary I continued to find it that these unfamiliar things (the yellow and russet nineteenth-century *palazzi*; the millennia-old city's Brobdingnagian buildings; the dark-crowned umbrella pines, as expansively outspread as poppies in full bloom; the steps of the Faculty of Architecture, on which I stood for a few minutes to listen to the rumble of time washing over me; the tree-lined avenue we walked down after having visited the university; Campo de' Fiori, that June evening, and the queer contrast between its conventional evening-piazza's languor and the gloomy statue of Giordano Bruno) ... that these unfamiliar things had once been his, had once belonged to the world of that young man who was as unfamiliar to me as they were, that young animal who was still free and innocent and for whom I felt an almost fraternal affection – I who was older now than he had been when he left here (and that was incredible, that was incredible too). And I wondered what these things had been like, seen through his eyes, and what texture they had had, for him; and what had the Battle of Valle Giulia been like and the long months that followed; and what had L.B. been like, at that age, at that moment in time, in those places?

But that, I realised, was impossible to know – about him or, for that matter, about any existence that wasn't my own.

And he was certainly harder to piece together than other people – other people who had at least left documents, letters or diaries in which they expressed something of themselves, other people who had managed to preserve their memories, other people of whom there remained something more than fleeting impressions left on third parties. Surreal: I knew almost as little about the workings of my father's mind as I did about my deleted ancestors – and that little was via intermediaries. I hated the idea of how much had been lost: I wanted the whole life, in its concrete entirety. I wanted to salvage all of it, even while knowing it couldn't be done. The singularity, the unrepeatable complexity of one ocean wave among all the others, of one forgotten day in the life of a man. Of a single pair of eyes blinking. And at the same time: how many hours, days, conversations, meaningless encounters, or incidental ones, combine to form a life? It was a towering, vertigo-inducing paradox. But daftly (and also, I think, quite naturally) I continued to want it all the same, that totality. I longed to re-evoke the totality; and instead I found myself piecing together a story full of holes, piecing together an insignificant speck of dust on the huge and bloody grindstone of history. A story in which the one thing missing was always the voice of the central character.

How ironic to think that I had, until very recently, spent many rewarding years thinking about him as little as possible, successfully erasing the more unpleasant memories of those summers when I had loathed him, and of his illness, and of, therefore, almost everything else. It's so true, isn't it, that at some point the dead always do come back to visit us, and we have to sit down at that table with them.

Every morning, L.B. and Druina woke up at five o'clock and went off to hand out bulletins at the gates of the Factory. The previous day's news, picked up at the start of the afternoon shift: what was going on in the body shop, what was going on in the paint shop, etc. There were so many departments and so many workers, and the Factory was so improbably vast, that this was the only way information could be filtered from one department to another. The long road, with its vista of the mountains (which on bright days stand out so clearly in the sky above that avenue – which is empty now, which no one walks down any more – that they seem so close you could touch them, beautiful and poignant and pure), that long road on to which the Factory's gates opened had, from 1969 onwards, teemed constantly, all day long, with people, megaphones, pamphlets, gossip. At two o'clock, when one shift ended and the next began, they came back to pick up that day's useful news, and on it went, over and over again, in an endless loop.

In the evening, the party members met up at headquarters and each of them described the places they had been to, and what they had learned from talking to the factory workers or the women at the markets, and what was happening in various neighbourhoods and in the other factories. But their day often didn't end there: there were times when, at one o'clock in the morning, they set off in a group on adventurous fly-posting expeditions, because it was illegal and they couldn't do it by daylight. They slept three hours a night, if they were lucky. L.B. and Druina would get into the car and traverse the city's wintry darkness well before the factory workers had even begun to leave their homes.

I can picture L.B. in those foggy dawns, with an overcoat too long for him, his hair uncombed, a big scarf round his neck, talking to one of the still half-sleeping people who are filing past in that long, mute procession, handing them a leaflet or a newspaper, ribbons of icy breath leaving his mouth. Did you ever feel lonely and tired, with your comrades beside you, on a crepuscular winter morning in front of the Factory's gates, while bleary-eyed workers trooped past you, pushing you away, perhaps, with a brusque gesture, with a blunt word? Or perhaps the fervour of their creed was more powerful, and L.B. simply felt very alive, felt that this was the right place to be, felt inspired? How cold was he? Did he have someone to love? Did it ever feel awful?

The thought of standing in front of the Factory's gates at six o'clock in the morning feels awful to me.

And yet there was also happiness, in that odd, exhausting way of life. They were forever dashing backwards and forwards, they were forever talking – about the future of mankind, or about nothing in particular – they and their comrades (including members of other organisations) met up in cheap restaurants, and they teased each other, and they went to the cinema, and they listened to records, and they sang together and bickered, and read novels the party certainly wouldn't have approved of, because they didn't come anywhere close to being edifying enough. And there was a sort of electricity, a closeness, an unfailing warmth, an inexhaustible mutual curiosity. And then the intoxicating thrill of the protest marches, of the speeches (L.B. was a brilliant orator, he loved speaking in public, he seemed born to do it). And if, amid all this hustle and bustle, it suddenly got very late and you hadn't found a bed to sleep in: no sweat. You slept on a couple of chairs in the local party office, or on benches, and at the end of the day who cared? They were all so young. They were all so happy.

They had a very simple slogan: *Bread, peace and work*. The darker and thornier issue, namely the fact that the road to revolution was necessarily lined with violence – armed violence – was left unexhumed. They never discussed it. They never talked about their own misgivings, not even with their most trusted friends;

nor were any of them in the habit of asking themselves too many questions. To admit any doubts was, a priori, to traduce the party line. Besides, their days were too busy for there to be any time to stop and think. The idea of that violence remained abstract and remote, a disagreeable background frisson which could be brushed off for now, like condensation on a windowpane. Thinking about it filled Druina's mouth with a metallic discomfort. She didn't know whether or not L.B. felt the same way, on account of the fact that they never discussed that kind of thing. But she had a suspicion he didn't like thinking about it either.

And also, up to that point at least, violence and crime had been the preserve of the other side. The fascists and the police. Sure, every now and then there were scuffles. Every now and then they fought back. But up to that point it had never gone any further. Apart from the death of that policeman in Milan, which, they decided, had been an unfortunate mishap. That hazy, nebulous mountain ridge must have frightened them, I think. And the things that frighten us get ignored. The present moment, their today and, at the very most, their tomorrow, were the only admissible horizon.

L.B. was faithful to the party line, but the party line didn't share his feelings. He wasn't much loved by the party leaders. They considered him a useful resource, but he was ill-disciplined and perpetually in their unwritten bad books. He had made too many friends outside the party, and the party considered all 'others' to be enemies of true communism – reactionaries, traitors to the cause, revisionists seeking reform and mediation: 'the ignoblest of compromises', their pamphlets scolded. The *Unione* was officially in the process of transforming itself into the *Partito Comunista Marxista-Leninista* and the hysteria surrounding their fear of 'fractionism' was at its most intense, appeals for unity were the order of the day – unity against all those 'others', who were secretly bourgeois, who aimed to sow division among the comrades; so the fact that L.B. was gadding about with so many different people who were off the central committee's sharp-eyed radar was an affront. He was continually accused of introducing rank-and-file or grassroots agendas into the party. It was the overarching goal that mattered, the promised land of the radiant future, and there they were, he and Druina and the others, worrying about mere side issues, about minor day-to-day gripes.

The truth was they felt ashamed, turning up at the Factory and spouting off about Mao when, in the meantime, right there, all that other stuff was going on. How could they stand there preaching to people whose problems included strikes, shifts, rest breaks, electing their own delegates, a minimum level of union representation on the shop floor? They wanted to write pamphlets that meant something to those people, not embarrassing little propaganda essays out of touch with reality (the newspaper they distributed covered that job perfectly well). And so they did. In fact, Druina was also called to order on a regular basis. The trouble was, they were very good at it, and the PCIM-L in Turin was relatively feeble, with very few members on the ground: it was hard to find a pretext for expelling them. Of all the local militants, they were the most active, the best at communicating with all and sundry, and the most persuasive – when they wanted to be. Agata talked about Druina admiringly.

'She was just like Leonardo,' she once told me. 'So brave and altruistic, always quick to side with anyone who was in trouble, always putting herself on the line.' Agata was sitting in an armchair when she said this, and she leaned forward slightly and stretched her arms out behind her, her palms to the rear, as though trying to imitate someone shielding a person in danger.

So that was what Druina was like; and also, it seems, L.B., who – Agata, again, told me – was generous to the point of recklessness, and threw himself into everything, body and soul, and was happy to pay the price. Or to put it another way, get arrested.

There are, in effect, various bits of news about L.B. in the local papers from that period: an arrest in January 1972, following a major police round-up in the Porta Palazzo area. A little Fiat 500 with loudhailers had driven through the streets blaring out: 'The police are fascists. Fellow citizens, do not let them search your homes!', and the carabinieri had stopped the car, only to find themselves surrounded in turn by a menacing group of a hundred or so local residents. A fracas ensued, leaving a few people wounded. One of the Fiat 500's four occupants was a certain Leonardo Barone, a twenty-six-year-old student who, together with the other three, was arrested for resisting and insulting public officers, only to be joined in the cells by the uncle of one of the other three, who had turned up at the police station yelling that either they got a lawyer or he'd smash the whole place up. By the end of the afternoon a group of extra-parliamentary politicians was on its way to the local prison to demand the quintet's release; a short while later the Public Prosecutor's Office granted them conditional release. Then he was on trial, in March 1972, for a picket at the L'Oréal factory, during which he and a handful of other 'troublemakers' had tried to stop the scabs from crossing the picket line and breaking the strike. They had also 'offended the carabinieri who were policing the picket'.

From 1971 to 1972 arrests and convictions for crimes of conscience had multiplied alarmingly. You could end up in jail for weeks or months while awaiting trial. And hundreds did. The privilege of waiting was reserved exclusively for left-wing extra-parliamentary politicians, lads doing military service, dissenting Catholics, and conscientious objectors. Its beneficiaries included a certain C.C., the heroic miner of whom Brandirali was so enamoured, who was jailed for a month and four days for having held a meeting somewhere near Caltanissetta in 1971.

In May 1972, Vanni Pasca, one of the PCIM-L's party chiefs, was arrested following a rally at the end of the electoral campaign in Reggio Calabria. Many people felt compelled to agitate on his behalf, and the various appeals for his release were signed by intellectuals, film directors, psychiatrists, journalists and politicians. A committee was eventually formed to push for the abolition of crimes of conscience, and, for the very first time, the PCIM-L found themselves working alongside other left-wing groups, jurists and democratically minded magistrates.

The affair also led to the episode connected with the photo I'd found from the trial for criminal defamation, the one with the bored female comrade and L.B. laughing with his head bowed. On 8 June that year, our indefatigable mischief-maker had gone along – together with the young woman – to the marketplace in Venaria, in a Fiat 500 (I assume it was the same one, but there appears to have been a whole fleet of them), and began distributing hand-printed leaflets protesting against Vanni Pasca's arrest. Meanwhile, their loudspeakers broadcast a tape-recording of 'Bandiera Rossa' and a speech criticising the government and Pasca's arrest. A plain-clothes carabinieri lance-corporal (this scene gets better and better!) had walked up to the car and asked if they had a permit authorising them to hold a public meeting. L.B. and his comrade had replied that they weren't holding a public meeting, and at that point, with a dramatic flourish, the lance-corporal had revealed his true identity and asked to see their ID cards. L.B. had his with him, she didn't. They were to come along to the command station, then, said the officer. Just a minute, I'll finish handing out the leaflets first, replied L.B., don't mind me. So the carabiniere went off to fetch reinforcements and, as he walked off, 'Barone would appear to have insulted the police,' through the loudhailer (in other words, he said something along the lines of 'fascist pigs'). Four officers then turned up and dragged the two of them off, and the woman appears to have shouted insults and put up resistance, and both of them ended up being sentenced, a year later, to four months and ten days for affront to public decency, and a further ten days for having held an unauthorised public meeting.

Venaria, Elia Morgari had told me, was somewhere they did a lot of work in that period. Back then, the central avenue and the old town it ran through was a grubby, run-down area where incomers from the south who worked in the factories surrounding the city lived crammed together like penned animals. And then there were the '*casermette*', the old barracks – grimy hellholes, again full of incomers, around a vast quadrangle of desiccated yellow grass and refuse. Entire families lived in the single rooms which had once been individual soldiers' lodgings. The ceilings were collapsing, the walls were stained with damp, the beds were often simply mattresses thrown down on the floor. Rats ran across those filthy, litter-strewn floors. Morgari remembered one lad particularly well, a young man with glassy eyes who already seemed strangely decrepit, and who lived in a ground-floor hovel literally overflowing with refuse that seemed to have been there for centuries. He left for work at dawn and came back, exhausted, to sleep, there in the filth, as if nothing could be done about it, as if this were his lot in life, and that was that.

The guys from the PCIM-L, including L.B. and Morgari, organised themselves into teams and attempted to help: they cleared the broken furniture and general detritus out of the houses, they plastered the cracks in the walls, they repaired things as best they could, they re-glazed broken windows, they handed out simple bits and pieces that permitted these people a more humane existence – blankets, clothes, soap, nappies, UHT milk, tinned food and occasionally some fresh food. They took babies to the doctor's surgery. And, while they were doing all of this, they explained why the revolution was necessary (couldn't they *see* why?). They were repaid with brief, tired, hollow words of thanks, and then they lost their hold on them again. They slipped through our fingers, said Morgari, almost all of them slipped through our fingers. His voice was forlorn.

In the summer of 1972, L.B. moved again and spent a few months staying with Emanuele Pariante – another PCIM-L functionary – and his wife. Again, she and L.B. left at dawn to hand leaflets out at the factory gates.

The rest of his time was dedicated to the unskilled manual jobs he'd been instructed to take in order to re-educate himself, and he handed everything he earned over to the party, which continued to pay him a small cadre's allowance; he rushed busily around, and he participated in all the factory sit-ins, and he gave his fiery speeches. And it was, in fact, during one of those speeches, while – still wearing his paint-splattered overalls – he fulminated from the steps of Palazzo Nuovo, that Cecilia Longoni saw him for the very first time. Probably in the spring of 1972.

She never could explain, nor could she remember, how and why they ended up as friends: they couldn't have been more dissimilar, and moved in completely different circles. Cecilia came from a good, liberal-leaning, provincial family, but once she started studying law in Turin she discovered that she found the left wing much more congenial, and soon joined the Italian Communist Party splinter group that produced the *Manifesto* newspaper. With three girlfriends who also came from well-to-do provincial families, she moved into a big and rather lovely flat in Via Petrarca, in the San Salvario quarter. Having seen the 'For Rent' sign, they had turned up there one day, at three o'clock in the afternoon, and found one of the outgoing tenants – a fifty-something pre-1968 leftist intellectual – lying fast asleep and naked on the sofa. The walls were plastered with Black Panther posters. As a matter of fact, some of the real Black Panthers had actually been to the house, possibly more than once: the owners of the rather lovely flat still hadn't quite recovered. They were delighted to be handing the keys to those charming university students who were so nicely dressed, with their innocent, round faces.

But then the girls' friends arrived. And the friends of their friends. You never knew who would be there from one day to the next. Amid the banks of smoke floating through the rooms, languid girls holding super-slim cigarettes wafted around with delicate Chinese dressing gowns draped over their shoulders (on top of enormous mustard-yellow sweaters); there were unemployed workers and employed workers; there were students – especially of architecture, which, for some bizarre reason, was the most politicised faculty – who conducted fervent debates until four o'clock in the morning (at which point either they got chucked out or someone lent them a bed); there were pensive and imposingly bespectacled mini-intellectuals; there were boyfriends and ex-boyfriends and potential future boyfriends; there were lovers and cats who wandered in from neighbouring courtyards, and L.B., who dropped by and chatted, and popped something on to the record player and read for a bit (he hardly ever had enough money to buy his own books, so he read at other people's houses) and then collapsed into a sleepy heap somewhere or other. On any given evening, at the table which was so long that it occupied the entire living room, ten or fifteen people could be found eating – often people none of them had ever seen before. With an admirable sense of practicality, one of the flatmates had eventually decided to charge a nominal 'working-man's' fee for those suppers crowded with freeloaders: five hundred lire, or you don't get to eat.

How L.B. had ended up joining that crackpot political party was something Cecilia didn't understand. To her mind it was already obsolete, it was calcified, it was unnatural; and he was too lively, too worldly, too funny and too chaotic to be a member of that churchlike group of fanatics. But whenever she asked him about it he waved his hand as though he were shooing off a fly, and said: 'Heh ...'

In the end she stopped asking him and they stopped talking about politics, because otherwise they ended up arguing. And yet, yes, they were friends – even if she was more pragmatic and had a better sense of humour, and he was a moony fundamentalist. They became friends the minute they met, and their fondness for one another was powerful and fraternal and lasting, even when their paths eventually diverged. It is still there, in Cecilia's bright and attractively sardonic face, which sometimes tautens when she mentions him, even while her mouth continues to smile. Friendships are the most undervalued element in any story; and yet it is often right there – in the inscrutable mechanisms, the hidden affinities which spark a friendship and keep it alive, in friendships that have no sexual or romantic overtones, in friendships despite the odds – that the most interesting pieces of a life play out. Of all the more or less autobiographical poems and novels I have ever read, the ones I have loved best have always been – and these are much rarer than you might imagine – those dedicated to friends (and by that I mean that they focus exclusively on them, so the friend is the sole protagonist or the dead interlocutor lovingly addressed by the poet, and the love the poet expresses is the kind that demands no explanations, the kind that stretches to embrace all of our own and the other person's failings, and the distances, the silences and the decades).

There was, unquestionably, something extraordinary about L.B., something spellbinding, something which all of those people I spoke to mentioned without quite being able to define it. It wasn't just his generosity, or charisma, or exuberance. It was a sort of purple fire, a mysterious radiance, a singular radiance all his own which immediately enchanted anyone it touched. 'His nobility,' Cecilia once called it, trying to find a name for that magical luminosity. I'm not sure that's quite it. The one thing I do know is that it was so bright that, almost fifty years on, the light of its rays is what makes it possible for me to write these words.

He took pleasure in everything, and above all in other people, whom he accepted and embraced in their entirety, and listened to, and offered the right words by way of reply; if ever anyone needed it, he bent over backwards to help them. One of his friends at the time lost his girlfriend terribly young – she was poisoned by the fumes from a gas heater they kept in their bitterly cold flat. Faced with the horror of that awful grief, L.B. didn't avoid him like so many people did: in the months that followed, he went round to see him almost every day, and brought him food, and listened when he wanted to talk. And when he couldn't face talking, L.B. sat with him in silence, for hours, in the dark room. He would do the same thing for many people, over the years.

But for all his many friends and acquaintances, for all his charm and apparent openness, and despite the fact that he was hardly ever alone, to those around him he would always remain strangely opaque and impenetrable. He was a good listener, but he very rarely talked about himself. He gave himself to others, but he also seems to have managed to elude them all throughout his life. He remained an enigma, always. No one can claim to have truly known him, someone once told me. No one can claim that with any confidence.

*

For instance. L.B. had always told his friends that his father was a judge, and that that was why he had stopped speaking to his father and the rest of the family. He said the same thing to my mother when he met her, and she only discovered it wasn't true when she took me down to Puglia, when I was a babe-in-arms, to meet his family, and spoke to my flabbergasted grandmother. L.B.'s father was just an *ufficiale giudiziario*, a bailiff who enforced court orders, a perfectly dignified occupation which allowed the family a modest degree of financial comfort and paid for their sons' education (the girls, of course, never crossed anyone's mind), and which meant that his wife, whose origins were very humble, was deferentially addressed as '*Signora*' when she was out and about in the town. Moreover, my grandmother had told my mother, he did that job – which was not always pleasant – with such tact and courtesy that he was universally respected. And it wasn't a smarmy pretence; it was sincere.

So why? Why tell a lie of that sort? A lie they all still believed when I met them. Even his lawyers. Even, one of them told me, the procurator in the trial for participation in an armed band, who had said, during one cross-examination: 'And to think, Barone, that your father was a judge! Do you feel no shame at sullying his name like this?' (But also, how could that happen? Weren't there documents or registers of some kind with details of parents' occupations? It certainly wasn't L.B. who mentioned it to the procurator. So who was it, then?)

I never did find an explanation for it – like so many of his weird, pointless lies. Before their rift, his father hadn't, from what little I know, been a bad father: he was rather kind and cared for his children; he helped them with their evening homework and polished their shoes every morning and left them by the front door, ready for school. 'I wish you'd known him,' my father once said to me. 'He was a good man.' He didn't add anything further. But the rift had happened. He definitely felt he had been repudiated, he felt he had been rejected for being what he was: and the pain of it, and the pain he in turn had afflicted by disappointing their hopes and by suddenly vanishing (possibly

131

as a form of unhappy revenge) were not things that could be articulated in those doctrinaire phrases which dominated the language he and the others used, that lexicon excised of all private emotion or ambiguity. Turning his father into the bourgeois enemy was easier: it was logical and romantic at one and the same time. The judge and his revolutionary son! Like something I later read in Umberto Silva's wonderful memoirs, talking about his militancy in the Italian Communist Party, the ICP: 'We were sons ready and willing to slay our fathers – our often very kind and occasionally very loving fathers – in order to submit to the will of the ferocious despot of the steppes and the ferocious despot of the Yellow River, who would both have hanged us for stealing so much as a toffee.'

I don't know to what extent they ever spoke again, or how. Then again, when you're young and everyone's eternal, you don't really think about these things, or about the unlikely possibility that the man you might one day find an excuse to make peace with could suddenly die, vanishing off the face of the earth together with his square-framed glasses and receding hairline and thin lips.

And that is what happened. In the October of 1972. *He'd seen him maybe only once or twice since moving to Turin.* On the 21st. It was the day before the big demonstration organised by the metalworkers in Reggio Calabria against the outbreaks of neo-fascist violence which continued to convulse the city two years after the revolt in protest at the decision to make Catanzaro the seat of the regional government. While the trains carried workers, men, women and youngsters on the long journey from the north of Italy to the south, towards the enemy-controlled city, along railway lines strewn with bombs that forced them to make continual stops and detours (there would eventually be fifty thousand of them marching, 'North and South, united in our struggle'), while, on the other side of Italy, this epic drama unfolded, L.B. took a train in another direction. Making his way, alone, to his father's funeral.

In the spring of 1973 a training session was held for Serve the People's party functionaries in Valganna, a little village in the province of Varese near the Swiss border, where the party had purchased a group of agricultural buildings which served as refectory and meeting rooms, and there were some small prefabs to sleep in, the bedrooms separated by simple sheets of corrugated iron to ensure there was no privacy. The training regarded The Issue of Sex, which was Brandirali's latest obsession: feminist discourse was beginning to filter through, even among the obedient and spuriously liberated ranks of the party's womenfolk. And in effect, while on paper they were the men's equals, in reality it was they alone who saw to the childcare and the housework and the sundry trivial chores that the men, who were too busy building the revolution, clearly couldn't lower themselves to worry about. So feminism was pernicious and had to be kept under control at all costs. Abortion was also regarded with suspicion, if not openly condemned; to say nothing of masturbation and homosexuality. Edicts had even been issued concerning the positions one could assume during intercourse (nothing too creative, lest they fall into bourgeois perversion) and oral sex, which was forbidden unless it concluded with *the act of copulation*. Orgasms, Brandirali preached, had to be simultaneous: the supreme expression of altruism and virtuous sex, strengthening the couple and improving each of them by increasing the enthusiasm of their dedication to the cause.

Love and politics were to go hand in hand, in an increasingly disturbing conflation, the culmination of which was the communist wedding. As is explained in *A Communist Wedding* – a booklet featuring transcribed sections of a recording of the first wedding celebrated by the party in January 1972: 'In the past many people thought that communism should not interfere in the field of family issues, as though there were ever such a thing as a private life isolated from the conditions of society and the class struggle unfolding therein. This was a grave error, provoking instances of corruption and liberalism among the comrades, and it was the women who suffered chiefly, remaining isolated from the party and very oppressed. Now, having waged victorious internal battles for unity, the Party is making headway in the private realm, and wants every comrade to recognise the validity of the communist vision in all areas of their life.' The bridegroom's speech gave thanks to: 'the Party which has given me more than even my mother has; I give thanks to the Party because, while my mother gave me life, the Party has given my life a purpose, it has given my life its lodestar, the Party has become my shield, it has become my strength, and I cannot but be grateful to the Party, I am grateful for the life the Party has given me!'

Sometimes the party even arranged the marriages, selecting the couples scientifically: the preferred combination involved a female intellectual (who needed to be proletarianised) and a working-class male.

The atmosphere at the training session was bleak. A violent collective psychodrama got underway, with people being compelled to make long and humiliating public confessions. Nothing was to be kept from the leading functionaries, not even the most squalid little details of their personal lives. Bachelors and unmarried women were obliged to self-criticise, the couples to describe their crises and their weaknesses and their sexual habits. Rivers of tears were shed. From Emanuele Pariante – who, two years later, would move to the United States for a while and ended up working in advertising ('I sold out,' he told me, grinning) – I heard about seminars on sexuality which he would subsequently realise had had echoes of the techniques employed by American advertisers (techniques which had conceivably been studied in anticipation of that particular training session), seminars designed to achieve what was to all intents and purposes a form of brainwashing, and simultaneously a display of power. Even the most loyal among them left Valganna shaken and disgusted.

It was just as the control over militants' lives reached its psychotic apex that the party began to fall slowly apart. Small streams of people quietly left, or were noisily expelled. Druina had given birth to a son in March 1973, and in the months that followed had distanced herself from the party, little by little, because she had ceased to believe in the PCIM-L; because the practical responsibilities of her day-to-day life – her job, the baby – were more concrete than the promise of a revolution which had started to seem increasingly implausible. The world was cruel: but she gradually became convinced that the solutions the party offered were the wrong ones.

'Never believe everything we tell you,' she said to me. 'People alter the facts. They choose which version of their lives to narrate. They forget.' Then she paused, as if mulling it over. 'There are three great human sins: mystification, envy and deliberately forgetting the things we're ashamed of.'

As for Elia Morgari, who didn't believe in the intrinsic rectitude of the masses, or that the expression of the collective will was necessarily a positive: he was brought to book repeatedly during their meetings, and accused of being a 'cosily introspective fatalist'. A perfect definition, he had observed with a little smile. He was tired of the PCIM-L's litanies, tired of all the ructions, tired of the constant lack of privacy, tired of the rhetoric. He had once, he told me, organised an activists' training session for Italian construction workers in Switzerland. Almost all of them hailed from down in Campania, and they essentially lived like slaves, sleeping in wooden barracks. He spent two days talking to them, at the end of which he was saluted with melodramatic farewells. There were workers who tore at their singlets and bellowed: 'I just want to see my family again, that's all I ask!' Morgari couldn't stand histrionics of that kind and had found it suffocatingly annoying.

'Maybe,' I said timidly, 'the pain was real, and that was the only way they knew how to express it.'

'Of course,' he said. 'You're right. But I couldn't help finding it irritating. And I felt guilty about that, too.'

I understood him much better than he imagined. I thought back to that conversation one evening, while N. and I were watching a documentary on the Italian *Gastarbeiter* in Switzerland (we were living together in Como, by then, and several years had gone by since I'd moved out of the little flat in Milan). In the 1960s, RAI, the Italian state broadcaster, had made a programme which they broadcast in Switzerland, in which the emigrants' families sent messages to their distant loved ones. Usually it was children sitting with their grandparents, and they weren't quite sure how to behave in front of the cameras. There was one young girl who must have been twelve or thirteen, a tall, big-boned girl with a message for her mother, to whom she wanted to say that she had started an apprenticeship as a seamstress. With a voice that quavered from the start, she said, 'When you come home, Mamma, I'll make you a beautiful dress, with all sorts of lacy bits.' Then her round face crumpled and she lifted her hands to hide it and said, 'Please, can we stop now, it's too upsetting.' I got up off the sofa at that point, and ran to the kitchen to cry. Once I started, the tears wouldn't stop. Was there any real difference between that young girl's bottled-up emotions and the emphatic men who tore at their vests? Wasn't the sentiment exactly the same?

Was there any real difference between my emotions and those of my father, which were by and large expressed so theatrically that I automatically assumed they were phoney?

Morgari had not been expelled from the party, despite his cosily introspective fatalism. It was he, in the end, who chose to flee that God-awful training camp. After one or two nights spent staring at the ceiling, he had decided he couldn't face any more of it. He stuffed his few belongings into his rucksack, slipped on his shoes and crept out of the prefab. It must have been two or three o'clock in the morning. He didn't have the faintest idea what direction he was moving in, but he walked all night through the woods, and by morning, exhausted, he managed to reach Varese. From there, still not having slept a wink, he took a train, and as soon as he arrived in Turin he went straight to party headquarters and leaned on the table and said, 'I quit.'

And yet despite all this, despite the brutality of the world around him and the grim and growing list of people killed, despite his father dying before they could make their peace, despite the arrests and the four months in prison for that moronic episode, and the privations, and the fact that most of what came out of the PCIM-L was devoid, as Elia Morgari put it, of any wisdom or humanity and impoverished the thinking of the party's own members, and despite the dark clouds of a potential *coup d'état* which hovered, invisible but by no means abstract, over all their heads, I am convinced that, for L.B., those were wonderful years.

He was living in an absolute present, in which any future was purely hypothetical (and what future isn't?), he was surrounded by affection, he was healthy and full of vigour, and there was still hope, considerable hope; it was sometimes unthinking, sometimes blind, but there was hope.

I wish I could leave him standing there, that young man. There for a few hours more, for a few days more. Hold him back by his sleeve, as if I were the ghost from *his* past. I wish I could lengthen those innocent months, slow the hands of the clock, leave it all intact for as long as possible – the faith, the joy, the blamelessness. And even the stupidity. But that's not an option.

It was 1973, and Chile came along like a baleful star exploding, and then the petrol crisis with its still-hazy promise of calamities to come. The cities went dark because the street lighting had to be switched off. My mother, in hospital somewhere in the provinces, underwent a second or third operation on her head. The jail in Turin was so full that there was no room left for the people they arrested, and even the provincial prisons soon ran out of cells. It was a dark, bleak winter.

It was 1973, and Christmas arrived at 13 Via Artisti.

Images of my father.

His freckled arm resting on the opened car window in summertime. The night trains we took together, the endless night trains from north to south and from south to north. Their acrid, dirty, metallic smell and the squeak of the paper bedsheets being pulled out of their wrappers; the speeding landscapes over which darkness rapidly fell, and which I watched from the couchette, lying on my tummy; the fairy-tale night-time glitter of the mountains in Liguria, which seethed with lights until somebody lowered the blind, and from then on the names of the stations the train stopped at, brakes moaning, remained secret; the little reading light over the bunk, which you had to push your book up close to if you wanted to manage to read; the sound of unknown people breathing. The funny dance he did in the posh sleeping car, that time we had a compartment all to ourselves (how did he afford that?), one that took us down to Naples where we were going to catch the hydrofoil ferry to Lipari. I was seven years old. He excitedly showed me all the wonders of that cabin, the real beds, the soft mattresses, the sink; he opened all the cupboards and all the little doors, until he accidentally opened a door into someone else's compartment. 'I beg your pardon,' he muttered, and then shut them back in. The silent marches down to the coves under the blinding sun, between cliffs dappled with juniper bushes and mastic trees. The gold and deep red of the late-Gothic Madonna della Misericordia who held her mantle open in a museum in Arezzo, and him standing in front of her, and turning round to look at me with an enchanted smile as I walked towards him. I remember the red behind his head, gleaming. Picking wild fennel in the fields at sunset. The garden at the house of those three sisters in Santa Maria di Leuca, which in the evening seemed as vast and mysterious as a forest or a dream. The sea-surrounded rocks we scrambled onto to rest when I got tired after a long swim, and the soft, slimy feel of the seaweed underfoot when the water was shallow enough for my feet to touch the sand. The mesmerising lapping of the water. In and out, in and out. The path that led up to the house in Lipari, on that last holiday we spent alone; it wound through the fields and the stones. It was dark, and we were coming back from a supper at someone's house – English people, I think – and there was a very strong smell of jasmine, and we were talking … what were we talking about? I think it may have been bats, because one had just flown over our heads. But I couldn't really remember.

It had been a long time since I had thought about any of these things, but over the course of the spring when I found out about L.B. they started coming back to me at odd intervals, at the strangest of moments: when I was on a tram, or doing the washing-up, or walking down roads where the cherry trees and magnolias had blossomed, or coming back in after an evening out – walking home, more often than not, even when I was a long way from my flat, because I loved the length of it, the way time expanded in the quiet streets, the illuminated windows of the houses, the yellowish light of the streetlamps behind the dark, deep foliage in the night. (I have never walked as often, as far and as unnecessarily as I did in those two years when I lived in Milan.)

So, that was how they came back to me: quite randomly; and then they almost immediately melted away, flickering. And the constellation they formed was disjointed and illegible. They were like those stereographic scenes from nature that people used to look at through binocular viewing devices in the nineteenth century: they emerged from the blackness, with no link between one image and the next, and with an illusory three-dimensionality which gave me no real sense of their meaning or of their depth.

I, who had always been convinced not just that I remembered almost everything, but also that I had understood – that I *possessed*

– the things I remembered, suddenly found myself bewildered by what I remembered.

I couldn't extract Lipari from my memory in one piece. It emerged only as splashes of light wrapped in a sort of rosy mist which was blurry and impenetrable, and the same thing was true of the period when he lived in the attic, which was even remoter; and the sense of impotence resembled the feeling I had the first time I encountered the idea of death. As I fought to remember, for some inexplicable reason an old picture book resurfaced from the darkness of the attic, a book of fairy tales I used to read when I went round there; it had been the only children's book in the flat. Left behind by a previous tenant, perhaps? Apart from *Wildcat Under Glass*, there wasn't a single other object I could call to mind, a single colour or detail, if not the semi-darkness of those rooms. Two rooms, or maybe three. Yes, three: one of them had been occupied for a few months by a young man who looked like an Indian holy man with a long, black beard, but I think I only saw him once, sitting cross-legged on the floor of his room. He had smiled at me and waved. Then he, too, had vanished. I thought about the book. A fuzzy vision of one of its pleasingly old-fashioned illustrations was floating around in my head. It must have been the fairy tale about the brothers who were turned into swans by a curse. Or perhaps I was confusing it with something else. I couldn't remember, I really couldn't remember. I had no idea what had happened to it in the end – it must have been left behind in the flat. All of a sudden I felt a silly, illogical, piercing nostalgia: I wished I could read it again, like I sometimes did with the storybooks at my mother's house. Somehow so very beguiling simply because it was lost – and also because it was the only object visible in that hazy dimness – that book became a symbol of a lost life, of that life erased; as though it were bathed in all the light that life emitted. Which was perhaps the reason why, all around it, only shadows and uncertainty remained.

I had a nagging sensation that there, in those far-off and now inaccessible moments, something important was lurking, and that they contained within them an enigma that I was no longer able to decode. Or perhaps there was no enigma: but I couldn't access them in any case, nor would I ever again be able to. So, I just couldn't know. Also because I was the only person left who could have remembered it, even that little fragment.

The effort itself, the heaving struggle to remember, was another enigma. Why worry myself so much over events which were so irrelevant and arbitrary, so unrelated to one another or to my present-day life, and above all, so unrelated to the story I was trying to tell?

But Lipari continued to hover – aching – in the air around me.

The couples formed under the aegis of the PCIM-L had included one made up of C.C., the poseur mentioned in the novelist's book – the Sardinian miner in his fifties who recounted his past battles with such Zolaesque enthusiasm – and a thirty-year-old teacher of Italian who lived in Rome. We'll call her Adele. He can be Cabras – his surname. The first of the two Cs was the initial not of his Christian name but of a nickname he was known by. A proletarian (albeit now a party functionary), and an intellectual: the perfect combination, according to the canons of the central committee. To begin with she indubitably found him attractive: the other women told me he had a lot of sex appeal. He was a tall man who walked with broad strides, and he had a face not handsome but imposing, primitive; and a resonant voice and a romantic past. But all of this soon ceased to excite Adele: not long after their relationship began, he started to beat her savagely and to torment her incessantly with wild scenes of jealousy, until one day, taking her newborn baby who bore the same name as his father, she decided to escape.

The party removed Cabras from the area, sending him back to Carbonia. Adele moved to Turin and started teaching at the middle school in Via Artom. Her flat in Via Artisti was sparsely furnished but cheerful, overflowing with propaganda material, with pamphlets and with copies of the party newspaper, and she often had friends and comrades over for meals. She received frantic letters from Cabras, full of threats and barely comprehensible, but she forced herself to ignore them. She was a sensible person and she thought the world made sense.

He asked if he could visit her in Turin, for the Christmas Eve meal at the end of 1973. The baby was almost a year old at this point. Adele decided to let him, because, despite everything, she thought it was right that a father should see his child. But she did ask two friends to be there, just to be on the safe side. One of them was L.B.; the other was a lad who'd become a great friend of L.B.'s over the previous few months: a twenty-three-year-old party activist, an engineering student to whom Adele was renting out one of the rooms in her flat. His name was Roberto. He came from Riva del Garda. In the only surviving photograph to have been made public, a grainy black-and-white newspaper photo, he has an attractive face, broad and smiling, an amused twinkle in his eyes. Dark hair with a side parting. Everyone loved him: he was affable, kind and funny, and he was gifted with a lightness of heart that was a far-from-insignificant talent amid all the grey, monastic dreariness of the PCIM-L. He wrote poetry, and it was apparently rather good. And just the previous month, he and L.B. had been the witnesses at the wedding of two of their party comrades: Roberto for the bridegroom, L.B. for the bride.

They had been happy to hang around. They were convinced that, with two men in the house, Cabras would hold himself in check, if he were thinking of freaking out. Who knows why they were there in Turin, at Christmastime, and not at home with their families? According to the newspapers, Roberto had also lost his father recently. Three people who were on their own, offering one another protection.

Cabras arrived in the afternoon and was charming and very cordial. He and Adele played with the baby and he stayed on for supper. He poured out generous quantities of the full-bodied red wine he had brought with him from Sardinia, and narrated his fascinating adventures to the two young men who, despite themselves, listened enthralled. He was, after all, an old-style communist hero: in 1948 he had taken part in the miners' strike in Carbonia, when they occupied the mines for sixty-five days, and he had spent six years in jail. He was a real old-guard revolutionary. None of them noticed, as the hours went by and they downed glass after glass, that he didn't touch the wine. None of them noticed it there and then.

After supper, and a dessert and a final exchange of pleasantries, they walked Cabras round to the bed-and-breakfast where Adele had booked him a room, and when they came back, she asked her friends if they would both spend the night there. She still didn't feel entirely safe. They said they would, and then they may have had a last glass of wine, to reassure her that everything was normal, the unpleasant chore had been done, there was nothing to be anxious about now. And then they went off to bed, each in a different room. Adele slept next to the baby's cot, as she always did.

But Cabras came back at half past two in the morning, not knowing that the other two men had remained in the house. He had a butcher's knife with him. He got in somehow – I don't know how, but perhaps they'd left the door unlocked – and went straight to Adele's bedroom. Hanging over the cot there was a poster which said '*Buon Natale*', Merry Christmas, with red stars surrounding the words. Cabras walked up to Adele's bed, and may have paused for a moment to watch her sleeping, to contemplate the thing he was about to destroy, and then he bent over her and started stabbing. She woke up and screamed. Indescribable screams that ripped the skin from the motionless air of that quiet rainy night.

A dishevelled Roberto was the first to arrive, wearing just a T-shirt and a pair of underpants. L.B. followed close behind, and when they entered the bedroom they saw that, like a patient butcher, Cabras was sitting on the bed. Adele attempted to lift herself up, and he threw her back down and knifed her again. There was blood everywhere, all over Cabras, all over Adele, all over the bed, all over the floor, all over the wall. Roberto instinctively threw himself forward, but Cabras swung round at the very same moment with the knife in his hand, and sank it into Roberto's chest, right up to the handle. And then, just as calmly, pulled it out. Roberto stumbled, lifted his hands to his chest and, pressing them to the wound, looked round at L.B. who was standing, frozen, at the door. L.B. grabbed him and then, holding him up, led him as far as his own bed, where he laid him down. The blood had soaked through his T-shirt and continued to spurt.

Strangely, Roberto was lucid. He said, 'I think he got my aorta. I'm dying. Get help. Call an ambulance.'

L.B. hesitated and there was a moment of silence. Then the shrieks from the other room recommenced: she was fighting to free herself while he continued, like Fuseli's incubus, to press her down and to knife her. L.B. launched himself at the man and managed to throw him to the floor, wounding a hand in the process; but Cabras got straight to his feet, swaying, his face no longer that of an old goat but demonic now, glowering, horrifying, dripping with blood, like something spawned by the very shadows of that wretched winter. He lunged forwards, but L.B. managed to dodge him and raced out of the flat in his pyjamas, shoeless. He knocked on the neighbours' doors, crying for help, but no one – not one person – answered. So he went out into the street and began to run.

The young man runs through the night. He runs across the city, runs through the endless city. Tomorrow is his twenty-eighth birthday. The city sleeps on in the rain, unknowing and oblivious, its shutters lowered and its windows closed.

The earlier masks have fallen; new masks will come. For now, time and the man are suspended. Everything he was, before tonight, disintegrating. He is stripped bare, terrifyingly free, with a wild freedom, reckless and unrequested. He is terrifyingly innocent. Blood, blood, blood. The only true *fact* shining into the night is the blood.

Perhaps his feet will be wounded, running like this, without shoes, without socks, on the asphalt. Running. His face tonight is invisible. His entire body a mechanical action pressing on towards where, towards what. How long the city lasts. The same streets as always, the streets of the living day, now unreal and unseeable and unfamiliar. Not one bar or restaurant is open: he has no idea what to do. He is innocent. He's scared. He knows nothing yet. He already knows it all. Forever.

The young man runs through the city of stone.

*

He ran through the rain for miles. Without encountering a soul. Until he got to Elia and Druina's house. He clung to the doorbell until one of them answered. They came out into the street and saw him trembling, glassy eyed, his pyjamas smeared with blood: a preposterous apparition, a hallucination out of some Gothic novel. L.B. confusedly tried to explain what had happened. Morgari wasted no time on replies: he ran upstairs to grab him a jacket, threw it around him, and led him to the car, to take him back to Via Artisti. In the meantime, Druina telephoned for help.

When the police entered the flat in Via Artisti, they found Cabras still sitting on Adele's bed. They arrested him immediately and he didn't so much as flinch: he calmly explained that she should just have listened to him, that was all. Adele, incredibly, and despite approximately fifty wounds to her legs, arms, chest and lungs, was still alive. In the other room, though, Roberto was dead. But it hadn't been that first wound which killed him. Cabras had gone to find him, lying moribund on his bed, and had finished him off by stabbing him a further three times. They took Adele off to hospital, where she underwent operations and transfusions, and in the end, a few days later, was pronounced to be out of danger. She survived.

***

There is a photograph of the young man – L.B., my father – taken that night by a journalist from *La Stampa Sera*. Someone must have lent him some clean clothes. He is wearing a light-coloured jumper and a windbreaker with the zip half open. Two men are standing behind him. One with a hat, and one who's looking at something beyond the edge of the photo and twisting his mouth in what looks like a grimace. On the left, there's the open palm of a hand: it's someone who's talking; the two men are listening to that person. He isn't, though. His eyes are fixed on the floor. He isn't looking at anything. He has a split lip, an Elastoplast on the bridge of his nose, and his hands are folded in his lap as though he doesn't really know what to do with them. Those hands are almost out of view, but we can see that one of them is bandaged.

I want to describe L.B.'s face in this photo. Apart from anything else, if I want to feel my way to guessing something of what he was feeling, these photos are the only evidence I have. But I realise I can't find the words for it; the words crumble as I reach for them. It's empty: it's an empty face. It's a face I can't bear to look at for more than a few seconds. And then I have to look away.

On the evening back in February when Agata had told me about that Christmas night in 1973, in those last few minutes just before we went our separate ways, my original reason for going to meet her and the information she had heaped on me in the hour beforehand, all that mass of information, had acquired a secondary importance. Via Artisti would extend over the rest of it like a nebula for a long, long time to come. I had walked home very slowly that evening, beneath the deserted porticoes, my hands making fists in my pockets, my head bowed; I had edged forward charily and frightened, as if I were having to learn how to walk again from scratch, while everything I had understood of an entire life disintegrated.

I remember stopping to buy a newspaper just before the kiosk closed, and the voice of the young man who sold them, and my voice too, seemed otherworldly.

More than any other thing, it was Via Artisti which gave me a sense of the scale of the abyss that separated the man I thought I had known from what he must, in reality, have carried inside him. The distance between the surface of the lake and the unseeable, unreachable rooftops of Kitezh.

My mother had never known about it. I had known nothing about it. Via Artisti was just a few streets away from the house I'd always lived in. How many times had we walked past there together?

For many nights afterwards, alone in my bed in Milan, I lay awake in the dark thinking about that young man running, my heart bursting with the sadness of it and with pity. He was his best friend, Agata had told me. What must it be like to cradle your best friend's head while he bleeds to death? What must it have been like to abandon him to his fate and to have to escape, and sure, it was to find help, but to abandon him *anyway*? What contours could a person have after something like that? I couldn't imagine: my imagination refused to advance across that hideous and unavoidably abstract piece of terrain. All I knew was that my brain froze when I thought about it, and the stabs of pain reached my temples.

I wondered how many times, on how many nights, he had curled up in a ball, defenceless, and had relived those scenes, and hadn't been able to cover his eyes to block them out, and there had been no relief from the aching clot of horror and shame in his chest. I should have stayed behind, he repeated robotically when people tried to talk about it. I could have saved him. I should have stayed behind, stayed behind, stayed behind, stayed behind, stayed behind, stayed behind, stayed behind, stayed behind, stayed behind, stayed behind, stayed behind ...

Of course there was nothing he could have done. Had he stayed, he would have died too, that's all. But telling him that over and over again was useless. He nodded, and then his face clouded over again, and went back to being expressionless and remote.

Even today, everyone who took part remembers Roberto's funeral being ghastly. There was so much grief; but there was also the terrible shock of that unreal event happening in the narrow little world of the party. That senseless murder – and the near murder which Adele had survived by sheer fluke – had been committed by one of the very group of individuals whom Brandirali had transformed into the ideal personification of the angelic, courageous, generous purity of the true proletarian; it had been committed by a legendary, heroic miner. Comrades, moreover, do not kill comrades. They never did establish why Cabras had gone back to finish Roberto off: to leave no witnesses? But he knew perfectly well that another witness existed, and had got away, and had seen everything. And there was also a credible possibility that he had intended to hand himself in anyway.

Agata's theory, which wasn't so far-fetched, was that he had planned to put the bodies in the same bed and pass it off as a 'crime of honour' (a mitigation which would only be abolished a few years later), although there would have been a technical snag: he wasn't married to Adele – whom the newspapers accordingly called 'the man's former lover'; and he was described as the man 'who killed for love'. In any event, and whatever his motive for having murdered a young man he'd never met before, throughout all the stages of the trial he never stopped blaming Adele and the party, who had firstly sealed their union and then imposed their separation even though he had wanted to marry her. And before making his way to Turin, he had prepared a letter for their son in which he explained to the child that his mother was a whore.

But he hadn't managed to kill her. Once she'd recovered, Adele and her baby went to stay with Elia and Druina and their son, and lived there for some time; she was frightened of being alone even for a few hours. And a witness did exist: L.B. There's a photo from the appeal trial a couple of years later, where he's talking, and his face is agitated and at the same time filled with sorrow. The former comrades were careful to avoid saying anything in Cabras's defence; they actually accused him in no uncertain terms of being a fascist. They had known he was violent and that he molested the female militants, but it was later discovered, they told me, that two decades earlier he had also abused his young daughter. Cabras was eventually sentenced to twenty-eight years' imprisonment. Not life, because the judges didn't take the premeditation into consideration, despite the letter to his son which did seem to indicate that the idea had occurred to him in advance. 'He killed while blinded by passion.' I haven't found his death reported anywhere, but I assume he didn't leave prison alive.

L.B. once took Agata to Roberto's grave in Riva del Garda. He stood for a long time looking at the tombstone, with his hands in his pockets, not speaking. The wind ruffled his hair and the hood of his windcheater slapped against his cheeks. They were the only two people in the cemetery, or so it seemed; the sky was big and grey, and the mountains around them looked like hunkering giants.

'If I had just ...' he said at one point, his voice miserable. She squeezed his arm, leaned her head on his shoulder and gently signalled no.

I *should have stayed behind, stayed behind, stayed behind, stayed behind, stayed behind.*

This is a story no one remembers now. Just one of those ugly episodes reported in the crime news, relegated to the back of the newspaper archives like most of the crimes which are no longer of interest to anyone, because the case was closed the night it happened. There were no supplementary mysteries. It was of concern only to the people who had survived and would have to live with it for the rest of their lives.

I thought about the woman. Adele. About what it must have been like for her to carry the burden of Roberto, the burden of the fact that he had died to save her – which they only told her about once she had recovered. I thought about the horror which must have clung to her like a viscous filth. About the terrible scars she would have had on her body for ever afterwards, reminding her every day of what had happened to her, even when she didn't want to think about it. I thought about her son and what kind of life he could have had after all of this. I hoped he had been happy, I hoped they had both managed to be happy, somehow, and had prised themselves free from Via Artisti. They told me that she had remained involved in the movement in Turin for a few years afterwards, militating in the feminist groups; then she had moved to Milan and possibly got married, but no one knew where she was.

I did try looking for her name in the telephone directory online, but half-heartedly: I wasn't so sure I really wanted to find her. And again: what would the point have been? To remind her once again of that horrific night? Of course, she was another one of the people who possessed a piece of my father, but I knew that this particular piece couldn't be uncoupled from what had happened to her. There were three Adele S.s in the phone book. The hair on the back of my neck stood up: one of them, the one in Milan, lived in the tree-lined square a few hundred yards from my flat in Milan. Seriously? Over forty years later, all that separated us was a five-minute walk?

In the end, after much anguished mental debate, I rang the phone number for that address. Waiting for someone to answer, shaking, I wondered what I could say, and whether or not I was doing the wrong thing. But an automated message told me the number was no longer available.

The following day I walked round to the door of the building. I wasn't sure I would have the courage to ring the bell, but I wanted at least to know if she was still there, if she was alive. Assuming it was her. But it was one of those intercom set-ups without buzzers for the individual flats, just a number pad you keyed the code into. I went off to sit down on a bench. In a way, it was a relief.

Once, when I was with some friends who had come over from Turin to see me, and we were walking back home on a midsummer day, we walked through that square and passed an old lady who looked like she was more or less the same age Adele would have been, and I stopped for a second: there was something in her features that reminded me of Adele's in the photographs I'd seen in the newspapers. But perhaps the resemblance was just a figment of my regret.

We walked on, going our separate ways, the old lady and I.

The second time I met up with Agata it was at her new flat, towards the end of April. I'd never been there before – it wasn't the flat with the long, shared balcony where you could see the church spire. This one was bigger and in the loveliest quarter of Turin, where whole streets of art nouveau buildings survived the bombings that erased half the city at the end of the Second World War, and everywhere you look there are ornate bow windows and neo-Gothic front doors, and stuccowork and stone animals and panes of coloured glass. Agata was happy to see me: she showed me all the rooms, including those of her now-adult children, one of whom was about to finish university and was currently in Belgium, and the other was in his last year at school; it was a beautiful flat, elegant and well looked after. She told me that her daughter's enormous gentian-blue wardrobe was one of the pieces of furniture that she and my father had been given when they got married; it was still pristine, forty years later. The kitchen furniture came from that former life too, as did the two pictures hanging next to the front door – hectic charcoal drawings of workers, done in the style of Guttuso and given to them by a painter friend. They had hung in every house they'd lived in. And in her bedroom she kept a blanket chest and an olive-wood-framed mirror that came from Monte Sant'Angelo. So there *were* a few objects that had once belonged to L.B. still in existence somewhere. And they had become part of other people's lives, adapting themselves to those other lives, but remaining testaments of a sort all the same: I liked the idea.

Agata made some tea and served it in the living room, sitting me down in an armchair facing hers. On the coffee table there was an old and very full photograph album: she opened it up and showed me the sepia-toned photographs of the day she and L.B.

got married, in the October of 1974. Everyone in them looked very serious – contrite, even. I caught a glimpse of my tiny grandmother and my aunts and uncles, and I saw Agata's family: her younger brother and her sister, her mother and father. It was only at the point when they were signing the register that their faces brightened a little. Zia Ziella was there too, and was the only one of them crying the sentimental tears a relative ought to cry at a wedding, and the expression on her face was fifty per cent Anna Magnani and fifty per cent St Teresa of Avila. Agata was wearing a trouser suit – of which she gave me an elaborate description, telling me where it had come from and all about the detailing – and she looked much older and much sadder than she should have, having just turned eighteen. Her witness was a wan-faced blonde girl, a member of the PCIM-L who'd been imposed on them by the party. L.B.'s witness was a professor of architecture whom he'd met – thanks to his assiduous fraternising with people from the faculty – at the assemblies where he often gave speeches. L.B. was wearing a light-coloured suit with bell-bottom trousers, and in the photos outside the town hall he was smiling with rather more conviction. Agata also looked more relaxed.

Then there were other photos, photos of holidays, the rough-and-ready holidays they took, setting off without any particular plan, and doing it on a shoestring in groups of ten or fifteen people who often slept on the beach or camped in the pinewoods; and then photos on somebody's boat, possibly in 1975 or '76, in the Tremiti Islands. She told me the people's names and stories – what had happened to one of them and what, as far as she knew, had happened to that other; and she told me about unhappy love stories and about romances which worked out well in the end. There was also Cecilia Longoni, with her sister, in one of the photos – the girl with the flat in Via Petrarca – with her short hair and a scowl on her face, like a little child. She was sitting at the stern of the boat with her elbows on the pushpit rail. It would be another year before I met her, and she would later tell me about a time when they'd sailed around the Gargano Peninsula in a friend's boat – perhaps the one in that photo – and it must have been around the time L.B. had been reconciled with his family, she said, and at one point they had heard shouts from one of the beaches, 'Hey! Hey!' and there was L.B. swimming joyfully towards them, incredulous, well look who it is, I don't believe it, they couldn't believe it either, it was too prodigious a coincidence. They pulled him aboard and anchored the boat there for the day. There were photos from Greece in 1980, with Misa and Ester, and Altea still a few months old, a roly-poly little thing wearing a cotton sunhat. And in one of them a curious L.B. was watching a cook preparing something on a big horizontal spit. There was a photo, this time in colour, of the wedding of a friend from the law faculty at some point in the 1980s. And there he began to look like my father in the version I had known, his hairline beginning to recede, the odd grey hair on his head and in his beard.

Then Agata told me the second part of the story I wanted to know, and at times her eyes filled with tears. That was the day she told me about Druina, sitting in the armchair with her arms flung out behind her. She was, in a way, narrating an ending, and it was a very painful thing for her to describe – not the end of her marriage, but the conclusion of many other things. It was strange to think that the end of their love story had resulted in my existence. But I really don't think that ever crossed her mind. She was very happy – and of this I am absolutely convinced – that I existed: firstly because I was my father's daughter; and now because I was who I am. She actually said a curious thing to me once: that she was sad her father had died before I was conceived, because it would have given him great joy to know that Leonardo had a child. And yet, to begin with, he was far from happy with that marriage – because Agata was too young; because he didn't want her involved in politics (he was afraid she might get into trouble). But despite that, he and L.B. had evidently become rather fond of one another later on.

When she had finished, Agata said to me: 'There's something I want to give you.'

I followed her into the kitchen. On the table there was a long white envelope I hadn't noticed earlier; she began to pull out other photographs.

'These,' she said in a voice thick with emotion, 'are from his childhood and teens. Your father left them with me; he forgot to take them with him. I've always treasured them. Now I want you to have them, all of them. I've made photocopies, so I can remember what they're like even if you've got the originals.'

I took them and, taking a deep breath, started to look through them. The only one with a date on the back – April 1956, so he was ten and a half – was a photograph taken for a document of some kind. A very handsome and very solemn little boy, his wavy hair combed with the parting to one side, dressed up for the occasion in a smart jacket. In another one (it must have been taken on a junior school trip, said Agata) the same young boy, with his eyes screwed up because the sun was in them, his face pink and dotted with freckles, his fringe mussed up and hiding his forehead, a stripy sweater and the air of someone who had stopped for a second while running; a teacher wearing glasses with tinted lenses had a hand on his shoulder, and behind them there is the sharp curve of a beach and a cloudy sky. And then the last one: the young boy is skinny, in a bathing suit, his hair wet, sitting on the sand with his hands in the water, one leg bent underneath him and the other stretched out, a smile illuminating the faded black-and-white and filling the flat sea behind him, and reaching as far as the bathers on the horizon. The young boy with my face; the happy young boy at the seaside.

But the one that struck me most was another passport photograph in which he seemed to be about twenty; so, it must have been taken sometime between 1964 and 1966: it was getting very close to the beginning of the story I was reconstructing. He was unrecognisable – even less like himself than he had been as a little boy: a handsome, severe-looking young man, his hair still in a side parting, a dark V-necked sweater, his eyebrows thicker now, but still straight, his sideways glance penetrating, his lips full. I'd never seen him without a beard or moustache. I was disarmed by that noble, smooth-cheeked, unfamiliar face. It didn't look like him and was, therefore, a new identity – which had a strangely violent and interesting effect on me; an effect similar, in some ways, to that of the notice of appeal: there, in that little photograph which fitted into the palm of my hand, he was wholly L.B., the stranger.

'He's so handsome,' I said, astonished.

'Yes, he is, isn't he!' said Agata. We smiled.

I looked at the photo of the young man again, then at the photos of the little boy, and then put them back, one by one, in the envelope. So here he is, then, the ghostly and imaginary little boy in the fog of the town on the mountaintop, whom I had never managed to picture, and who now began to take shape. Or rather, here is the longing, yes, the longing: lost love, love never known ...

Life in Milan progressed, in some ways, just fine, even if it didn't actually give me the impression it was progressing; I experienced a persistent sensation of immobility, of expectation, which I didn't understand. Can you spend your entire life in suspense? When I didn't take sleeping pills, I slept four hours a night at most, and was forever exhausted and bilious; and when I took them I had hallucinations as I fell asleep and spent the whole day in a state of drowsy torpor. But I continued enjoying my walks and the encounters with new people who then became friends, and the visits from my mother, whom I took to exhibitions and on aimless tours of the city and out to eat in my favourite places; and I continued to enjoy my weekends with N., and my near-empty flat. I hadn't hung anything on the walls and I hadn't done anything to make the place mine, apart from the few dozen books I'd managed to squeeze into the little bookcase: that was all I needed – a space that represented my newly acquired freedom.

I had begun to do some work for other publishers, so I read all day long. In the morning I got up and made myself a coffee, and got dressed, and then, regardless of what the weather was like, I went out to a café or a library not too far from the house – although, on nice days that weren't too hot or too cold, I happily lengthened my walk, or stopped for a bit to sit on a bench in the park – and I read manuscripts. In the evening, before supper, I wrote up the reports, report after report. If I wasn't going out for the evening with someone, I worked on after supper, late into the night, especially in the weeks when the book fairs were on and the manuscripts poured in. This didn't stop me reading for pleasure. I read vast amounts: I caught up with all the Italians who, in recent years, I'd almost completely ignored in favour of

American writers (and then Jewish and Israeli literature, and then the English and the French, and then finally the Russians). I read Giorgio Manganelli, Michele Mari and Anna Maria Ortese, who staggered me and whose writing I fell hopelessly in love with, even if her ecstatic lyricism irritated me sometimes. And Juan Rodolfo Wilcock, who may not have been a real Italian but might as well have been; and Lalla Romano, Tommaso Landolfi, Goffredo Parise, the Primo Levis I'd skipped, Natalia Ginzburg, Dino Buzzati and Marina Jarre. And there were others I discovered: Clarice Lispector, Danilo Kiš, Aleksandar Hemon, Martin Amis, Annie Dillard, Julio Cortázar, Magda Szabó. I read a few contemporary Italians, in an attempt to overcome the idiotic prejudice I'd always had, but also because some of them had become friends of mine and I was curious to see how they put their ideas into practice on the page. I reread the things I loved best, and continued to discover something new in each of them every time. And I read essays and eyewitness accounts and documents about the years in my father's life that I wanted to write about, and I dug out films from that period, and film clips and documentaries. I read constantly. My head was overflowing with voices. It was wonderful.

I no longer felt I'd missed out on anything – a PhD, for example: the idea of a life in academia didn't appeal to me, much though I had loved studying literary theory, and much though I'd loved the lecturers with whose help I had discovered it – but I still wasn't entirely satisfied. I had a dim feeling that time was passing and that I wasn't doing anything to carve out a role for myself.

**

I fantasised about something which I envisaged resembling the community of writers, critics, painters and poets in St Petersburg in the 1910s and '20s. Or the Russian émigrés in Berlin and Paris, or the intellectuals of Turin in the interwar years and the '40s and '50s, or the post-war French. Not insular groups united by an artistic ideology, which I didn't find remotely interesting, but composite, fluctuating groups, meetings of very different minds who steadfastly retained their individuality but also read their poems out to the others, or read out passages from their novels as they progressed, and discussed them late into the night, and always met up in the same places, creating that incessant, protean, exciting exchange of ideas that I adored whenever I encountered it in those writers' memoirs and papers – like Shklovsky's unforgettable description of the House of Arts immediately after the revolution, where there was someone thinking, working or chatting to somebody else in every room, cocooned in as many blankets as they could get their hands on and half dead with hunger, and, 'from the staircase, the dark of the staircase, up rose the poet Osip Mandelstam', who was muttering the lines of one of his next poems under his breath.

I once said as much, rather tentatively, to a friend of mine, a writer and translator fifteen years older and more cynical than me, who had been involved in the earliest experiments with online journals but had then let it drop. We were having a coffee while taking a break from the library, and I thought my voice sounded very young and inane as I talked about how lovely it would be to meet up in a group like they did fifty or a hundred years ago, and to read and debate face to face, which was something I felt the lack of.

'We tried that, years ago. But we gave up. That kind of thing doesn't work any more,' he said.

'Why not?'

'I could give you any number of answers. But in all honesty, it just doesn't. That's just the way it is. Nothing like that exists anywhere any more – not even abroad, if we're honest.'

I pursed my lips, peeved, and didn't insist. I mean, for heaven's sake, they'd even managed it *in Turin*.

My romantic fantasies were obviously unrealisable. Even if I didn't really see why they should be. It seemed we could only meet up in groups of three or four at the most – and four was already a major event. People's homes were sacrosanct. We only ever got together when some petition was doing the rounds in response to an infelicitous event, or money was being collected for something, or to express our indignation, or to mock someone who'd made a minor or serious gaffe or had written a mediocre book or article, or one that was presumed to be so (or – and this never failed to surprise me – to heap praise on some equally mediocre book). The authors moaned that nobody read them; the translators moaned that they were overlooked; the critics moaned that contemporary fiction was dreadful and that no one took criticism seriously enough; the children's writers moaned that they were never considered 'real' authors (and on that count one could hardly claim they were wrong), and they fenced themselves in in a form of corral from which they yelled out their indignation, regardless of what real or putative talents they actually possessed. There were the usual, tedious, antediluvian quarrels between those who maintained that intellectuals had a moral obligation when it came to civic engagement, and those who said no, intellectuals had no moral obligations (the automatic inference – I took malicious pleasure in noting – being that they themselves were members of the category). And all the generational discourses ('the onus is going to be on *us* to ...') left me wanting to run off in the opposite direction. There were magazines and journals, but that very rarely led to flesh-and-blood encounters between the people who read one another's work with any pleasure. It was, and it still is, a paltry era in which any display of emotion or intellect could only ever happen with one other monad, sitting at a little table in a bar, or on the phone.

There were no letters any more: none of us would leave behind collected correspondences like the ones that still existed a couple of decades ago, venting our impressions of famous or not-famous figures, our private jokes and our own thoughts on writing. What would remain of us all? Every now and then a friend and I would say: we should write each other letters. But the idea never came to anything: we continued just sending texts and emails which never got much further than a formulaic, 'How's things?'

For a while there was a project which vaguely resembled what I had in mind, organised by people from the publishing company I did consultancy work for: you met up and took it in turns to read an extract from a book you found 'sad'. One learned a lot about other people and about authors one hadn't read. But there were only five meetings or so, in the end. At one of them I read Katherine Mansfield's *The Escape*. Another girl, who at the time worked for the same publishers, read a piece from Ingeborg Bachmann's *The Thirtieth Year*, about the anguish of feeling time running out, and being confronted with the fact of having a single path to follow and no longer having an infinite number of choices. She was pretty, blonde and looked very sad – in keeping with the evening's theme. Outside in the street I told her that, to me, that particular worry seemed very remote, if not inconceivable: one day, much later on, she would remind me of that conversation, with a smile.

But I liked all these people so much; I found them all so interesting. More than they would have wanted me to, I suspect. And ever since I had begun to wrestle with L.B. and all the people I was talking to about him, that curiosity had ballooned like the rose in Magritte's *The Tomb of the Wrestlers*, which ends up filling an entire room. It felt like I was beginning to see people properly, and that the strange detachment I'd experienced in recent years (or always, maybe?) had loosened its grip on all those faces and lives. It was still there, though: I was perfectly well aware that I continued to live much of my life in the abstract. Reality mushroomed around me, but I was still a spectator. I still couldn't see why the streetlights floating in the fog in Via Paracelso on an evening of thick fog should make such an impression on me, or the ridiculous spires on top of the Institute of Chemistry (the 'Kremlin of the university district') with their aquamarine pinnacles suddenly emerging from behind the treetops; or why my mind sometimes wandered off for no rhyme or reason on those arbitrary retrograde journeys, of which all that remained with me afterwards were the light trails, a glint of the blue of the sea, a night-time path on an island, the shadowy light of an attic, the sprawling temples of Paestum quivering in the white-hot air of an August day; I felt it, but didn't explore the feelings: they were still just scattered images, still just something vaguely noticed.

And so, in the October of '74, L.B. and Agata got married by superior order, and began their life together in the cold, inhospitable flat in Villar Perosa that she hated so much. From that entire period – when they certainly couldn't afford a camera – all that remains is a single black-and-white photograph, a tiny, blurry photograph which Agata recently found at the bottom of a drawer and gave to me with apologies for the fact that the quality was so bad. Who knows who took it? L.B. is there, sitting in a very bare kitchen, wearing a jumper and a shirt, with a hand on his chest: his face has faded – it's almost invisible. All you can see is that he has a moustache and is smiling. Looking at it, I found myself hoping that for him, for them, that life which was so exhausting, so poverty-stricken and harsh, might also contain a few moments of joy.

The recession dragged on. The prices of bread, meat, sugar and petrol increased almost weekly. In some sections of the housing projects militants from the extra-parliamentary left wing organised 'auto-reduction' – partial payment – of electricity bills and rent, which would spread like wildfire through almost all of Italy's big cities, becoming a very real weapon in the fight against high living costs. And very often the workers from the electricity board who were sent to cut off the supply to those homes then didn't do it, out of plain solidarity. 'Red markets' sprang up all over the place, with people selling essential goods at very low prices, 'political prices' they called them. And the first of the furloughed workers also appeared – anomalous creatures forced into an aimless and potentially endless quiescence, who drifted around the city lost and confused by their sudden nothingness. Inside the prisons a rapid succession of riots broke out, and sometimes inmates who had already surrendered ended up getting shot. For the very first time, the Red Brigades went so far as to kidnap a judge, but the State refused to negotiate – despite the beseeching letters which the judge wrote to just about anybody he could think of. Thirty-five days later, they freed him anyway.

There was the referendum on divorce, and there was much jubilation when the noes won and the divorce law was not repealed. Genuine heartfelt jubilation. And then there was the second bomb, in the piazza in Brescia. And the third one, in August, on that train.

That was also the year in which Agata succeeded in convincing L.B. to write his thesis and to graduate with honours. I came into possession of that thesis only two years ago; for some reason, he'd left it at the house of a woman he became friends with in the 1980s. As Agata had told me, it regarded the connection between bronchopulmonary and pleural tumours and the social environment. I read it with a certain degree of interest. For its time, when the search was still on for a suppositional cancer 'virus', it was rather advanced, even if its subtext was inexorably political: in fact, at one point L.B. writes quite explicitly that the continuing research into a mythical virus was very convenient for employers, who thus avoided taking responsibility for what they may have done to their employees. Citing Dulbecco, he also evaluates the possibility that some types of cancer might be caused by a virus, but most of them, he maintains, are undoubtedly the result of cellular degeneration triggered by environmental factors.

For a few months, after graduating, he worked with the *Istituto di Anatomia e Istologia Patologica*, doing research for them. And then at some point (we don't when or why) he stopped.

The brief Strada delle Cacce interregnum was about to begin: the last of all the battles L.B. waged from within the party.

Strada delle Cacce ran through one of the new social housing districts which had been built, with the support of the Factory, on the edge of the city. It was a singularly ugly spot, totally isolated, with no street lighting and no shops, a very long way from the last stop on the bus line, with unmetalled roads which, in autumn and winter, turned into a semi-permanent quagmire across which the area's five thousand inhabitants, almost all of whom were incomers, moved using torches and galoshes. An error had been made when the pipes were laid, so they had been dug up again and had yet to be made right, and the road looked like a bombsite. The children, in their hundreds – these were all families of six or seven people, or even ten – had to walk for miles in the mud to get to the nearest schools. And walked back home in the dark along what was basically a warpath. And if they ever went off to play ball games somewhere nearby where the streets were actually tarmacked, they got chased away, because heaven forbid they might break a windowpane; so the only fun available to them was sailing paper boats on the water in their quagmire, in what was effectively a sad parody of Parisian children at the fountain in the Luxembourg Gardens. From time to time, thank goodness, an occasional distraction presented itself: like that time, for example, when a removals van got stuck in the lake of mud and rubble, and a bulldozer had to come and pull it out. The refuse collectors seemed to have forgotten that Strada delle Cacce existed; and as for the doctors: most of them refused to make home visits, in order to avoid crossing that swamp.

Nonetheless, the still-uninhabited newly built homes surrounded by all that sludge were the focus of the feverish dreams of thousands of people. Twenty thousand, to be precise, give or take a hundred. Who had all of them put in applications at the Chamber of Commerce for one of the two thousand two hundred and forty flats, there and at Falchera, which was the other district recently developed by the IACP, the *Istituto Autonomo Case Popolari*, on the other side of the city, in the outermost northern suburbs. The new tenants were to be selected using a points system based on the size of the family, the number of years for which they had paid into the social security system, the state of the primary householder's health, the state of their current lodgings, etc. The trouble was, they were all in similar straits: evicted,

164

made redundant, living in families of ten crammed into one or two rooms with a bathroom out on the gallery balcony (shared with all the other tenants on the same landing), and paying rents which were higher than was decent; and young workers who'd arrived just recently and would never acquire enough points, because they had the misfortune of being in good health and of having made only a few months' or a couple of years' worth of payments into the system. Ah, the cruelty of criteria! How does one assign points to desperation? Which bedbugs were worst, which hovel was grimmest, which rats were the most ferocious, which landlord sucked the most blood?

Twenty thousand applications, and all the members of each of the families behind each one of those applications: how many people must there have been? An entire new phantom city of non-inhabiting inhabitants which the other city, the official one, the *real* one, the metropolis of the factories, had ingested for decades, like an insatiable mouth, without ever once asking itself – if not too late in the day – where they were to be put, where they could live that wasn't just a living tomb. A real home, a home fit for human beings! Even if the watery swamp was still out there, along with the solitude and the sempiternal distance between them and the 'others'.

Within the space of a single day the selection process was begun and completed, and the sentence dropped like a stone on the heads of the excluded, who were ten times the number of those to whom a lodging was assigned.

Approximately three weeks later, sometime in the night between 26 and 27 September 1974, Emanuele Pariante, together with a group from the PCIM-L and other extra-parliamentary left-wing activists, broke down the doors of the still-empty and as-yet-uncompleted social housing units in Strada delle Cacce. At that particular point, L.B. wasn't there: he arrived on the scene a few days later, Pariante told me. At dawn they let in the occupiers: one hundred and twenty families – men, women, old folk and children. Almost all of them arrived from the sodden, rat-infested hovels which were still to be found in the area around the old toll gate at Barriera di Orbassano in between the new blocks of flats built in the fifties and sixties. They carried bags containing their few belongings; it was all they had. The committee that had been formed to oversee the occupation had rigged up a big floodlight to illuminate the various floors of the buildings while the families settled themselves in. Straight afterwards, most of the men – who were nearly all factory workers – went off to work, while the women stayed behind to guard the flats and to light fires in the courtyards with the activists' help. The contractors who were working on the buildings in Strada delle Cacce immediately reported the occupation to the authorities, and the police and carabinieri surrounded the neighbourhood, ready to move them all out as soon as the order arrived. But then they withdrew. In the following days, there was a constant toing and froing, with people bringing food, clothes, blankets, heaters, bottled gas and clean water; and new families of occupiers arrived all the time, many of them workers from the Factory.

The intention wasn't to take the houses away from their legitimate assignees, who wouldn't have been able to move in before mid-November anyway. They knew full well that the others were just as poor as they were, and just as much in need. They indignantly refused to play the disgusting little game of 'war among the wretched', of which everyone had immediately begun to talk: it was just an act of symbolic protest, they declared on the Sunday, at the Mirafiori 'House of the People', when, together with a large group of local workers from the same neighbourhood, they met representatives from the city council, the regional government and the IACP. It was just a demonstration. Something that finally and definitively released them from the hypnotic inertia of the *inevitable*: this is just the way things are, it has always been like this and it always will be, you just have to accept it, again and again and again. This is the life that the celestial bureaucrats have, for some strange reason, assigned us; we didn't accrue enough points.

But to the National Association of Tenants, the IACP and the GESCAL national workers' housing trust, life's inherent scandals were of no interest; those people were squatters and they had to leave. The protest's organisers were equally intransigent. The occupation would end only if and when a temporary but decent solution was found while waiting for new homes to be built for the people who'd been excluded during the allocation process – for example, they could requisition the thirty thousand flats currently empty in Turin. Not in ten years' time, not in twenty years' time: as soon as possible. And so, for the time being, they weren't going to budge an inch.

A delegate from the ICP took the microphone, to say that the issue of housing couldn't be resolved like this, that it was more 'general', that there was a need for wide-scale mobilisation; and at that point someone interrupted him, shouting that he'd spent a lifetime being told that what was needed was strikes and wide-scale mobilisation, and so why didn't they do it then, these strikes and mobilisations, and everyone would get behind it. They never did.

Pariante decamped from Strada delle Cacce almost immediately, but L.B. stayed on. While the PCIM-L was elsewhere, unravelling, he pursued that forlorn and gruelling battle, accompanied by a tiny group of militants from the party and others from Communist Struggle.

They organised the occupation taking the factories as their model: each stairwell had its own delegate; they set up rotas for picketing the stairs; they exchanged daily updates regarding the problems encountered by whoever was already there and whoever was arriving; they ran assemblies and made sure that all the squatters participated equally in their shared battle and that no intruders who weren't in urgent need of accommodation took advantage of the situation and slipped their way in.

A few days later another occupation began in Falchera, and the IACP immediately handed the keys to the legitimate assignees. But in an unexpected move most of them took the side of the 'squatters', recognising that this was a battle which concerned all of them, that their own good luck had been random and didn't make the others' needs less sacrosanct, and they rejected the divisiveness of a points system that they themselves considered arbitrary. They called each other comrades, and that word, which could have seemed corny and stale, acquired a fresh purity, a fresh intensity. They understood that this thing wasn't just of concern to those particular neighbourhoods or a single city; it was something that involved them all – the eternal injustice and the injustice of the present situation – the whole country, their own humanity, and that still-obscure catastrophe which they sensed approaching, of which the signs were already visible, and against which they wanted furiously, desperately, to fight right to the bitter end.

It was a long autumn. The entire city was ablaze with occupations, and the housing crisis was rendered all the more dramatic by the fact that the crisis in the construction industry was at its worst and there was no likelihood of improvement in the short term. Work had stopped on all the building sites; thousands of construction workers risked losing their jobs because there wasn't enough money in the coffers to guarantee even their furlough payments. The only thing happening was protest marches, endless and fruitless meetings between the City Council and the squatters' representatives, continual postponements in order to win time; and responsibility bounced back and forth between the competent authorities. No one gave an inch: the City Council wanted the flats vacated immediately, and only then would they contemplate discussing possible accommodation for the occupying families; the committees wanted a solution to be found simultaneously for everyone.

The cold weather arrived and the Strada delle Cacce committee made repeated requests for at least the water, gas and electricity to be connected. Up to that point they had made do with bottled gas to cook and to heat the rooms with, but it wasn't enough any more, the rooms were freezing. The sewers were still open to the sky: every day someone was taken to hospital with an infectious disease of one kind or another. The squatters went down to the aqueduct to protest, demanding at least that the flats be connected to the water mains, but to no avail. And then there was the fact that the boilers and radiators needed to be 'recertified' because the IACP claimed they had been tampered with. One week later, in Strada delle Cacce a four-month-old baby with a heart defect died of pneumonia.

Druina remembered that episode: she and the other women had gone along to demonstrate in protest at the baby's death, and they had blocked a road. Adele was there too, that day. The only one of them who ended up in jail – for a week, because she was known to be 'disruptive' – was, in fact, Druina. The families from Strada delle Cacce marched on City Hall and staged a sit-in, together with representatives from the factory councils from every quarter of the city, demanding a health inspector's visit and connection to the utilities without any further delay, and over and over again they repeated all the requests that the mayor had continued to sidestep: the requisitioning of privately owned flats which were currently vacant; housing for all, immediately; rents capped at ten per cent of salaries. The mayor didn't turn up until two o'clock in the afternoon, and at the end of the day he signed a memorandum of understanding with the committee, agreeing to house the families in three tranches: the first group within fifteen days, the second by the end of the year, the third by the end of 1975.

It was a partial victory, but what a sour one.

And so the waiting began, the long wait for those promises to be kept. One night, at what must have been just past six o'clock in the evening, but it was already dark, L.B. was – we'll imagine – sitting next to one of those fires that they kept lit in the court-yards like semi-permanent field camps, and perhaps he was all bundled up in a cap, scarf and coat; he was tired and was reading something by the light of the fire; all around him there were other people sitting silently, worn out at the end of a day's work or a day's activism. Maybe he would spend the night there, as he did occasionally when it got too late to go home; or maybe he would drag himself off to a party meeting, taking a bus or cadging a lift, and in that case he would sleep over at somebody's house; or perhaps he'd go home, to be with Agata, if she'd already got back in. If she'd managed to catch the bus to Villar Perosa in time. Or perhaps they'd see one another at the meeting. Neither of them had a car. It was possible that there wasn't even any food in the house. Every so often L.B. looked up from the book he was reading and observed the faces shimmying through the flames, the foreheads wrinkled under their caps, the hands thrust into thick gloves hanging forlornly between their knees. He knew nigh on all of them, even though there were hundreds of them now, but at times – like just then – he felt vaguely lost, as if he were very far away from the things of this world, from everyday life in the party, and even from them. And there they were, yes, they were sitting in front of him: but who were they? And he, who was he? What was he doing there? He felt an illogical rush of anguish and lifted his eyes to the deep, black sky, which was so big out here in the suburbs. But he lowered them again almost instantly: the sky was cryptic and infinite and it frightened him.

A little child was quietly moaning, swaddled in his mother's jacket; someone said something to somebody else that L.B. couldn't quite catch. But he wasn't listening. He was thinking. About right and wrong. He had always wanted to do good. That was why he was here. But he had the impression that this goodness never came to fruition. And what if it were just a fool's errand? What if all of this were pointless? he wondered. What did life amount to? Especially his own. What mechanism, what impetus propelled it forward?

'Do you want a cigarette, Leo?' the guy sitting next to him asked gently. Sebastiano, his friend from the party, the friend at whose wedding he'd been a witness, together with Roberto.

'Thanks,' he said with a smile, pulling a glove off to flick at the lighter, which was so cold that it only sparked on the tenth attempt. He put his glove back on and went back to staring at the fire. It made him feel strangely woozy, but that wasn't unpleasant. He knew it was getting late: he was wasting time. He should get up and go now ... Go where? He'd forgotten.

He had sacrificed his free will gladly, he hadn't thought twice. He had needed to. He had needed to because he wanted to do good. But now, in fits and starts, almost unconsciously, he began to sense that good no longer lay where he had thought it lay. That path was no longer clear and straight the way it had seemed to start with: it was crooked, abstruse, horribly false. It was so remote, the party was so remote ... so far removed from this fire at the edge of the city and this unreadable sky. And the old certainties were so remote. Where should he go? What should he do? Even freedom was frightening. He didn't want to lose everything he had.

But right now he was where he was, and what he was doing was right, he thought. Those squatters weren't perhaps, all of them, the loveliest of people, perhaps sometimes their instincts weren't entirely virtuous, and those unsound instincts needed to be suppressed, some control always needed to be maintained; but he knew that his being there for them was the right thing to do. '*Apprescindere*,' he thought in his southern accent. Regardless.

He prised his gaze away from the fire and turned it towards the dark of the street. And for a moment – perhaps because he had stared too long into the light of the flames – he thought he saw a stain emerge from the shadows, and it looked like Cabras's face; and Cabras's voice whispered mockingly, 'You know that good isn't always to be found where you want it to be.'

He whipped his head back round in the other direction and angrily stubbed the cigarette out under the heel of his shoe. He slipped the book under his coat. It was time he left.

I don't know precisely when the occupation of Strada delle Cacce finished. It's likely it lasted late into the winter, given that the City Council continued prevaricating and very few families had been assigned a home even by the time the second deadline arrived, and some of those homes were still uninhabitable. I have no idea when they were connected up to the utilities. Then Diego Novelli turned up – he was an opposition councillor at the time, and a few months later would become Turin's first communist mayor – all dressed in white, according to Sebastiano; and he offered to act as a mediator. From there on in it would be the ICP who took the reins and oversaw the allocation of the homes. Pariante told me that L.B. had returned to Strada delle Cacce very embittered, because he felt the campaign had been wrested from their hands, and for him that compromise was as good as a defeat: in all likelihood not all of them would end up being housed, although that had been their aim, right from the word go.

Over in Falchera, one of the most active members of the housing collective was Tonino Miccichè, a twenty-five-year-old Sicilian lad who was a member of *Lotta Continua* (Ongoing Struggle) and had worked at the Factory, but had been sacked following a politically motivated arrest. Possessed of considerable organisational skills and much enthusiasm, he had got everything running so well that they jokingly nicknamed him 'the mayor of Falchera'. A man who worked as a security guard and was one of the 'legitimate' residents had been accidentally assigned an extra garage, and the squatters had gone round several times to ask him if he would mind leaving the second garage empty so that they could use it for their meetings and avoid making a racket in the street late in the evenings; but the security guard had remained immovable. One evening they went round there anyway, opened the garage door and moved the car out. His wife noticed what was happening and ran out into the street yelling profanities. A few minutes later the security guard grabbed his pistol and followed her out. Miccichè walked towards them wearing a conciliatory smile, hoping to calm the wife down. The security guard shot him between the eyes. Miccichè died almost instantly, muttering something about not being able to see very well. Nine thousand people walked in front of his coffin in the funeral procession, before it was loaded on to the train which would take him back down to the south he'd come from when he was twenty years old. His death marked the end of it all.

His elderly parents came up to Turin for the trial and turned down the nine million lire compensation offered by the security guard, and on Miccichè's tombstone, high up on the wall of the columbarium in the village's little cemetery, they had the stonemasons write, 'Judge not the life here ending, but that which now begins.'

I drove down Strada delle Cacce one March, on a Sunday; it was a perfectly normal suburban street of tall blocks of flats, all them brick red and identical, with a patch of green running down the middle for the full length of it and three lines of trees. There was no one around apart from N. and me, and we got out of the car and spent a few minutes walking around in that unremembering place which told me nothing more than I already knew. We left almost immediately.

A man came over from Milan. He went to see L.B. and Agata in their flat and spoke to them at length. There was a current in the party, in the other city, who no longer supported Brandirali's line of approach, which was increasingly paternalistic, increasingly dogmatic, increasingly out of touch with the times. The only solution was to disband, to disband the party. There was no longer any alternative. He listed all the reasons for which the guys in Milan had come to that conclusion. L.B. listened carefully, and then, once the other man finally fell silent, he answered calmly: 'I don't need persuading. I agree.'

The death of the party was long, slow and agonising; in certain cases it also meant that, from one day to the next, entire families were left without the party functionary's stipend which was their only source of income; and for others it signified the loss of any meaning in their lives. What else was there, out there? What had they sacrificed their lives for, all their money, their ideals? In Turin, three women threw themselves off their balconies. There was nothing comical or liberatory in that harrowing and protracted demise.

On 22 November 1975, in Rome, Brandirali took the stage at the meeting during which they would officially disband the party. I don't know whether or not L.B. was present, but I doubt it. The founding father gloomily listed the two hundred and seventy-one missteps made by the party. And even though, until then, they had effectively always entertained the idea of a possible future violence, he concluded his speech saying that it was better to call a halt to it all at this point. Before the gathering darkness could swallow them.

And in the thick fog around them the shadows were indeed multiplying; it wasn't clear what they were, it wasn't obvious where they slid in from and off to; but in the night, in the cities, when even the last of the drunks had fallen asleep in the doorways and the last of the collectives' meetings had drawn to a close, if you were to have looked very carefully into the depths of the deserted alleyways, if you were to have stared for a very long time until your head began to swim, you would, for just a few seconds, have seen the chimera crawling slowly through the darkness, with its long body, its heavy, proteiform body, and its short scaly legs. And perhaps you would have caught a glimpse, beneath a street-lamp, of the creature's snout, of the tiny holes which were its ears, and its filmy, milky eyes swivelling blindly as it sniffed at the air to find its way forward, and its body, formed of a bizarre assembly of pieces of different beasts all glued together, across which there floated, like a slide slow, snatches of communiqués and statements in some incomprehensible language. It smelled of metal and blood and petrol, of adolescence and putrefaction, and of acrid, bellicose adrenalin. It shook its head, did the chimera, and its eyes continually filled with tears: it found its own exist-ence profoundly moving, its own stench inebriating. And then, if a courageous observer were to have hung around long enough, they would have seen it vanish back into the shadows, leaving only the lingering sensation of having had a strange dream.

In the May of 2015 I went down to Puglia for a cousin's wedding. I hadn't been back for six years. That last time had been a sad October, the October Celina died, and we had again gone down for a wedding. We had driven down, my father, Dora and I, but they had stayed on for a few extra days, and I had come back up north on my own, taking a night train. In the compartment it was just me and a woman who'd settled into the couchette beneath mine, and who talked a lot, in – for reasons I didn't understand – a nervy, urgent tone. Then she had fallen asleep. I hadn't. I had finished reading Kraus's *The Last Days of Mankind*, which I'd begun that summer and had abandoned three-quarters of the way through; and I remember the woman's gentle snoring, and waiting for the fleeting chevrons of artificial light each time we passed through a station, and reading in short bursts about that ghostly battalion of drowned horses re-emerging from the river to curse the general who had led them to their death, and then all the other apparitions presented in the final act. That was the last night train I had taken.

Instead, this train left at dawn, and it was much faster than they used to be. I gazed out of the window almost avidly, waiting for something to provoke a jolt of recognition. Hours went by, and then it happened: after Pescara, when the sea appeared alongside the train. The duck-egg-blue sea with streaks of pink; the calm, shallow sea of the Marches, which I had only ever known as a view seen in passing. But I recognised it. It was a cold windy day and the pale sandy beaches were still empty; here and there, the wind whipping their jackets, solitary figures with their hands in their pockets stared out at the water. At San Benedetto del Tronto the train passed a flower-filled park I didn't remember where people were strolling beneath the palm trees. And then (or before that?)

a rock-fall shelter, a sort of underpass which may have been taking us beneath the mountains and from which the sea was visible through huge stone arches. At that particular moment I had been in the buffet car getting a coffee, and the train had slowed down. I had turned back round towards the window and had seen them, and realised I had seen them before, those arches; I recognised them from the deep well of all those things we never paid proper attention to. The stations flashed past and their names were ones I had always seen early on summer mornings when the sun still wasn't fully up and I climbed stealthily down from my bunks to stand at the window in the corridor. The remembered names. Senigallia, Pescara, Francavilla al Mare. Here and there, the prehistoric carcasses of factories and abandoned hotels. And finally, suddenly, out stretched the Tavoliere, Puglia's vast central plain, with its endless yellow and emerald-green fields and the blades of the windfarms standing out sharply on the horizon – it seemed so far away, so infinite. Melancholy, solemn white giants barely moving their arms, because the wind had dropped.

I realised I had been leaning forwards, and sat back in my seat, letting that vision of calm majesty wash over me. I would have been lying if I had said I didn't find it moving; but not because I was 'returning to my roots' or anything as inane as that. This was the moment of categorical recognition I had been waiting for since I boarded the train: these were the lands of the little boy who lived up on the mountainside. And I came in peace.

The trip didn't last long, just three days. The time it took to get ready for the wedding (most of it spent sitting in the car with my aunt and my eldest cousin who were rushing off somewhere to buy or to pick up the last few bits and pieces), and then the photographs with the bride in her white dress in the smarter of the two living rooms in that house I'd slept in so many times when I was little and we came down to see them (a house now entirely inhabited by women because this family had lost their father too – the good-natured Michele, my father's favourite sibling, the youngest of the five and, by a malign twist of fate, the first to die, two years before he did), and finally the wedding and the lunch, and me stumbling around mildly embarrassed, and the other cousins whom I was seeing again for the first time in years (and their children, and the relatives who had survived, and the relatives who had changed, and the relatives who had aged, and the relatives who hadn't changed at all), and then, the next day, back on the train, back to Milan and the little flat where it was already dark by the time I arrived and the scent of the jasmine bushes filled the streets.

During one of those car journeys with my cousin, we had driven along the seafront, where the old city centre of Trani meets the water, near the cathedral. I had never really seen this bit of the city. The Trani I was familiar with was the area around their house, the new part, where all the buildings were tall, anonymous, concrete and recent, and the overpasses were papered with sun-bleached posters advertising passing summer circuses – the part where their maternal grandparents' little house also stood, with its patio and its long, narrow garden which was ringed with a low fence, and its thickly leaved trees through which the light passed in liquid diagonal stripes, and something old and abandoned that I remember finding enchanting (*possibly* a little round metal table, painted white but now peeling, like the ones in English novels where the garden chairs are all covered in fallen leaves). When I was a little girl that garden had seemed very big: seeing it again, walking past it (my aunt's parents were dead now and the house had been sold), I was taken aback, because it was tiny. Just a little patch of grass around the house. Had the trees been cut down? Had they ever existed? Oh God, I hated these cracks in my memory.

The old city centre, the old town clustered near the sea, was somewhere I'd only ever been once or twice. It was gorgeous, and I longed to have time to walk through those alleyways glimpsed in passing. From the car, my cousin pointed out the street where – further down, further up, from here you can't see it – our fathers' family had lived for many years. I wanted to see that too. But I couldn't stay on; I already had a train booked for the day after the wedding.

That yearning persisted, though, and intensified. As did my other, even stronger hankering to see Monte Sant'Angelo. It felt like a fitting act, a final act (wrapping up what, I couldn't have told you); the perfect ending for the thing I wanted to write which still hadn't acquired a shape of its own. Reconnection/completion. Coming full circle. I liked the idea.

So I went back that summer, with N., with the excuse of yet another wedding. This time we would stay for a week. We went down by car – another journey I wanted to relive. When we reached Puglia it was late afternoon and I was driving. N. had dozed off and I found myself confronting the Tavoliere alone, with big soot-black storm clouds racing across it. There was no one else on the motorway just then. I felt immensely powerful as I crossed that huge, empty plain: this time around I was running the show, I was the queen on the chessboard, and I would capture every piece I could. I wouldn't take my eye off the prize even for an instant.

*

But it wasn't what I'd expected. It was a fitful holiday, just like the weather: it rained and didn't rain in stops and starts, so the sky was almost always hidden behind a thick bluish-grey pall, which did occasionally break open but clouded over again minutes later. If we chanced it and went down to the beach when it looked like it was going to be sunny, after an hour or two the clouds would reappear and we would hear the distant rumble of thunder on its way. Most of the time we wandered through the narrow stone-paved lanes, going nowhere in particular: along the harbourside; down through the Jewish quarter which had prospered under the Swabians; out across the medieval fortifications and through the garden in the city park which had been built on a piece of terraced land rising steeply above the sea. We meandered past palm trees, pines and holm oaks tumescent with damp, and past benches standing in gigantic emerald-green puddles. By day the old town was placid and silent. In that lead-blue light the stones of the low, square buildings and piazzas were yellow and a blanched shade of grey, with pearlescent flashes of pink and pale blue; when the streetlamps came on in the evening, they turned the colour of old gold, and in the unlit alleys they grew dark as caves. At that point the patrons of the town's restaurants and bars swarmed on to the seafront and the calm began to fill with happy noise. During the daytime there was only, here and there, the occasional old woman in a sleeveless dress, sitting on a plastic chair on the pavement with her back turned to the road, and old men all wearing black caps and confabulating on a bench; to my great surprise, I never saw any children on the loose. On the second day, or perhaps the third, we visited the cathedral. When we came out, near the portico under the bell tower there was a blonde girl who was very thin and very young and was crying with big breathless sobs. Her face was red, and her eyes – which appeared to be blue – were swollen, as though she had been crying for some time. She was wearing a pale dress with little flowers on it. And white tennis shoes. I don't know why, four years later, it should be these details I remember and not, for example, the colours of the façade of the building that might once have been my father's home, or the words that N. and I exchanged. But at the time that girl, there, in that particular place, was a mysterious and incongruous presence, all alone, hugging herself, rooted to the spot and weeping like a Niobe turned to stone. Finally: something heartfelt. Something *alive*. I twisted round a couple of times to look back at her as we walked off towards the wharf.

We walked through the sleepy streets, and I scrutinised the buildings earnestly while N. took photographs. And I thought – as I've mentioned – that I had worked out which house my father's family had lived in. But those lovely, inert façades told me nothing; they didn't give me what I craved. Whatever trace memories it was I was looking for, there was nothing here. I examined my feelings conscientiously, but all that revealed was a chilly discouragement. It was like being in a hotel where the key to my room had snapped in the lock and there was no one at reception, and I was ringing away at the bell, ringing that bell, until the gesture lost all meaning.

On the fourth day we went to Monte Sant'Angelo, our real destination. The road that climbed up the mountain, flaunting the sheer drop below it at every hairpin bend, seemed to last for ever. I wondered how difficult it must had been to make one's way down from there, or back up again, with the transport they had available in the forties. Especially in winter. It must have been a very isolated place back then.

I'd never been there before. Or so I thought: actually, my mother later told me, I had been, but was too little to have remembered it. I had been five months old and it was the first time my parents ever went down to Puglia together. Of that holiday, a score of photos have survived, and I had often glanced at them when I flicked through the albums from my childhood: people my mother no longer remembered; a young woman on her own with a baby girl; a man with a moustache and dark curly hair; two girls who must have been about ten years old (both on the beach, but possibly in two different places); my mother and father sitting next to one another on a low wall with a line of drying washing behind them, both tanned, she wearing her usual, feline half-smile, a sleeveless dress in a flowery lilac-coloured fabric, her short hair bleached by the sun, a slender arm draped around his shoulders; in the next photo she has her chin on his shoulder, and he is smiling and saying something (one of the only two photographs I have in which my parents are sharing any physical affection). The others had all been taken by mother: the baby girl in the pushchair, smiling up at her excitedly and lifting her legs into the air; my father dipping the baby girl into the sea; my father sitting on a sunlounger with the baby girl lying belly-down on his knee while he reads a newspaper, both of them kitted out in cotton sunhats; and, finally, two photographs where, unaware he is being photographed, he is holding on tight to that scrawny, perennially sickly little baby and staring into the void with a lost, defenceless look on his face, as if it were him looking to her for shelter, as if the body of that baby girl were a lifebuoy and he was clinging to it. In the second of the two he is resting his cheek on hers, and lowering his eyelids very slightly. Those photos puzzled me.

There are no photos of Monte Sant'Angelo, though. Perhaps they were left unprinted on some roll of film, or had never been taken, or had been lost. My mother remembers him not saying much about it when they went down there together. He did talk about the history – about it having been a site of pilgrimage ever since the early Middle Ages, on account of the Basilica of St Michael the Archangel which was erected above a grotto and had been an obligatory stop on the crusaders' journey to war; and he talked about the snow in winter, and the vista, and the arid coast dotted with almond and olive trees, and the Foresta Umbra to the north-east of the promontory, which got its name from its *ombra* – its own shadowy darkness, the dense, dark foliage of its trees. But he never took me back there, when the two of us went down to that part of the world together. Or when we went with Dora.

So I arrived there knowing nothing, eager to be flooded with all the impressions possible. It was the day after the August bank holiday and the town was full of tourists and was every bit as unreal in its whiteness as I had imagined it, despite all the noisy, brightly coloured Bermuda-short-wearing reality thronging its lanes. It spread downhill in broad flights of steps and, with the exception of their exuberant chimneys, the houses were all so identical and regular that they looked like flat sheaves of paper. The further we got from the centre, the emptier and quieter the various corners of the town became. You'd have said the inhabitants had all vanished aeons ago, were it not for the occasional piece of washing hanging from the windows; perhaps it was because the sky was turning leaden again, but the façades of those houses seemed to grow whiter and whiter, milkily fluorescent. A cold wind got up: I only had on a lightweight dress and N. lent me his anorak. It was enormous on me.

'It's going to rain again,' he said, eyeing the dark clouds beginning to mass above the mountain.

'Yes,' I said, and he looked at me, because he'd heard the note of discouragement in my voice. He didn't ask me about it, and I was grateful for that. He simply gave my shoulder a quick squeeze.

'Let's walk on a bit further,' he said kindly.

I put my hand on his for a second and nodded, and off we went. But even as we wandered on through that daguerreotype of a place, nothing happened. No magic flowed through those streets, no revelation, no ghosts, no fatal flash of sudden comprehension. I stopped at a belvedere on the side of the town looking out over the Gulf of Manfredonia, and, with N.'s jacket wrapped tightly around me, I watched the storm coming in across the plain in vortical pale-blue columns, and the sea which was the colour of metal, and the flocks of dark birds cleaving through the lower clouds. I stood there waiting, with the wind slapping my face. Waiting, and asking myself what exactly it was I was searching for and why I'd failed to find it yet again. I didn't come up with an answer. And yet I had tried so hard to see it, to see it *intelligently* – by which I think I mean methodically. I had tried harder than I had ever tried to do anything, ever. The symbolic gesture I had attempted to make seemed to have been politely spurned by some capricious force more powerful than me.

It started to rain. In fat individual drops to start with, and then progressively harder. We took shelter in a bar to sit out the worst of the cloudbursts, and as soon as it began to let up we rushed back to the car, our feet sodden, now just wanting to get out of there as fast as we could. We were, both of us, very tired. As we drove back through the countryside towards Trani and our hotel, an opaquely puzzling thought struck me: my father hadn't been there. It seemed to be an entirely self-evident truth, as clear in my mind as those luminescent houses just before the downpour; but I didn't understand where the idea came from or what it was supposed to imply.

'That was useless,' I said miserably to N.

'You had to come,' he replied firmly. 'Even if it hasn't helped you. You had to come so that you can let this bit go.'

'I suppose.'

I sank back into the car seat and looked out at the fields.

I rarely thought back to that journey – most of us brush aside things that don't go the way they're supposed to. Until a few years later. Dora had given me a memory stick where she had saved copies of Christmas and birthday cards I had given my father and some photographs of my father in the last few years of his life, in places and with people I hardly knew or didn't know at all and so wasn't very interested in. Above all, I did my best to avoid the photos from the last year of his life – because I found them frightening, and was upset by that grey creature with his drawn face and increasingly huge yellow eyes, cocooned, wherever he happened to be, in horrible tracksuits much too big for him, even when he was sitting on a bench in the piazza or in a German forest, that last spring, when he had gone off to 'take a thermal cure' like an old-fashioned consumptive and wrote me fervent letters saying that he already felt better, that he was already feeling the benefits (and how small and alone he was in those photos in the woods, wrapped in his blue anorak, like the lost protagonist of a fairy tale in some old picture book, and how heartbreaking his frightened smile was).

That was why I didn't look at all of them and I put the memory stick away; it was only a couple of years later, when I was looking for something quite unrelated, that I came across it again and, quite by chance, opened up a folder from the summer of 2010. To my great surprise I found a series of photos taken in Monte Sant'Angelo. And there was my father, thinner than usual, but tanned and normal looking – the tumour on his liver had been removed at the end of May, after a week or two spent waiting in hospital on account of a string of transplants that meant the surgeon wasn't free to operate on him, a week or two which my memory had dilated to fill a suffocating month; he had just begun a cycle of chemotherapy. And he was standing on the same flight of steps and in the same piazzas I had been to with N. In two or three of the photos, I noticed, he was posing next to the front door of a house. I wrote to Dora to ask her if that was his childhood home and if he had gone back to Monte simply because he thought it was the last time he could, to say goodbye. She replied with a long rambling message in which she talked about that summer, about him wanting to attempt the long sea swims he was used to going on, I don't know if you'll remember, from the rocks at Scalea round to Baia del Carpino (yes, I did remember), even if he had to wear a T-shirt to protect his torso, because if he could manage to do the same things he'd done a year earlier, well then he could still allow himself to hope; and then yes, that was indeed the house he was born in. He had come across it by chance, while moseying around the town, and he was so happy and amazed that it was still identical sixty years on. He had even tried ringing the doorbell, hoping to see inside, but there were no names next to the bell and no one had come to the door – in all likelihood it was one of those houses just used for holidays now, and was probably vacant just then. Dora went on to tell me that he had had the idea of stopping off in Monte Sant'Angelo because, by one of those coincidences so bizarre that they trump anything you could ever invent, his oncologist came from there too, and they had discovered they were almost the same age and had lived in the same street and had attended the same school, in different years. Maybe he had felt it was a sign too important to ignore. And maybe the decision to go back had involved both things: the hope he might last a bit longer, and the feeling that the future was instead contracting irreversibly.

The last of the photos had been taken at the belvedere, and like a kineograph – those flip books that create the illusion of pictures being animated – they effectively tracked the transition from one state to another: in the first one he was posing on the edge looking out over the town, and was smiling; then, as he moved along the low wall towards the other edge, his face gradually became increasingly troubled and distracted; culminating in the final photograph where, standing on the same spot I would pause at five years later, his eyes stared absently at the vista, and his mouth narrowed in a sombre grimace. It was a heartbreaking image, but that tiny piece of magic – us both having stopped right there in precisely the same spot, at the same point on the belvedere (and I did make sure, I checked the photo N. took of me from behind) – made my heart skip a beat: I had been wrong; there had been an invisible and unknowing moment of contact. My father had been alive in the same place where, for a few minutes, I had been alive. In that alien town. In the town we had both missed.

Only then did I understand what it was that hadn't gone right during my expedition, and it really was a very simple thing: I had nothing to go by. There were no stories to give meaning to those places and there was no one left who could tell me any; there were no episodes I could reimagine and no details to bring back to life, no images that words could evoke for me. That un-recounted childhood had ceased to exist along with all the people to whom it had belonged, and before that – back when they still existed – I very probably wouldn't have been brave enough to ask them. It was gone.

Months after my Aunt Maria died (the last of the siblings, she had been suffering from some mysterious and possibly neurological ailment for almost ten years) I finally plucked up the courage to telephone my cousin Alida, one of her two children, Alida whom my father adored – he called her Alida the Injudicious, because she was always bubbly and breezy and animated, even in her moments of sadness. And she did remember a few things from the stories her mother had told her. It wasn't much, and I already knew some of it, but, little though it was, the vague flicker it generated rippled out to touch me all the same.

L.B. had been born at the end of the last year of the war. He had a hip malformation, a dysplasia, so one of his legs was shorter than the other: for many years, until he was at least seven or eight years old, he had dragged around a steel brace which entirely encased his leg and pelvis, and a plaster cast which was changed every month. Often the weight of it was too much for him, and his teenage sisters – who effectively deputised as stand-in mothers – carried him in their arms to the doctor's appointments. But like one of those little animals who lose a limb and adapt to the world by instinct, and demonstrating a stubbornness as precocious as it was unusual, he quickly adjusted his movements to accommodate that extra burden and learned to move relatively fast, running off and slipping free (a skill which, by now, dear reader, we can surely agree he would successfully conserve into the future), and scrambling doggedly up and down the punishingly steep little streets of the town, and the country lanes around it. It was literally impossible to pin him down.

One day he had snapped. He had taken off his callipers and had cracked the plaster cast open all by himself, employing God knows what tool and with heaven only knows how much stubborn fury. He had abandoned it on the floor of the kitchen and went out into the sunny day, leaving behind him a trail of rebellious white crumbs; and off he had run, to play football with his friends in one of the little piazzas. He wouldn't be reasoned with and he had never worn it again, despite the adults' furious tirades and despite the fact that he still had a slight limp – his gait would always be uneven, but you only noticed it if you watched him carefully. In part, I already knew this: it was the only fact of his childhood that he had ever, vaguely, mentioned to me. And Dora had told me about it, too.

After I was given that photo of the little boy on the beach, I had found myself studying the leg stretched out on the sand and wondering if that was the one and if someone had taken his callipers off to let him swim, or if he had already freed himself of them by then. That shining face tugged at my heart. However well he had managed to muddle along, it must have been horrible being captive to your own body at that age and for such a long time (and children's time is eternal, an endless afternoon with no shore in sight). I wondered if he had ever felt humiliated or helpless in comparison with 'normal' children. And he must have sometimes, inevitably. I wondered how badly that contraption had hurt, pressing against his soft, growing bones. I couldn't bear the thought of it: I felt a rush of protectiveness towards a little boy who had no longer existed for over sixty years.

But without that plaster cast he was finally free, and for the rest of his life he would never stop running. When school was out he went off on long forays into the woods where the shepherds took the animals to graze, woods thronged with beech trees and gigantic Turkey oaks, and ivy and feral cats; and off across the gentle swell of slopes which in springtime were sprinkled with campanula and buttercups and thistle flowers as far as the eye could see, and down into the valleys where the birds of prey nested and centuries earlier the pilgrims had passed, leaving them dotted with the ruins of rupestrian churches and grottoes; or sometimes, in the summer, he and the other children scrambled down the '*passi riponte*', the short cuts that led to the sea. Towards beaches which no longer exist, because time and human activity have eroded them.

Everyone called him Nardino.

As with his father, his feelings towards his mother remain an enigma. She I had known. My *Nonna*, my grandmother, 'the other nonna', the one I hardly ever saw. She appears to have always been too busy to make much fuss of her children; she was structurally incapable of showing affection. L.B. was much closer to his sisters than he was to her. There was a darker element to that invariably cool, practical and perfunctory relationship – one which, I think, he continued to carry within him – but no one knows much about it. My grandmother was a tiny woman who always dressed in black, with huge, thick glasses which made her eyes seem too big for her head, and short grey hair always carefully combed and teased. She wore tights, even in August. She lived in an old people's home her children had placed her in when she reached her eighties. We went to see her every summer and I never knew what to say to her because I didn't really know her; but my father also struggled. He kept his eyes lowered, he mooched around the room. I sensed his discomfort. She spoke in proverbs, mottos and phrases from songs. When I was sixteen she fell ill, and my father, Dora and I went down by train. He looked after her; he was solicitous, very worried and awkwardly affectionate. Sometimes he only seemed able to get on with people when he could nurse them. But when she eventually died I couldn't tell whether or not he was sad. I think they were so distant that he no longer knew what his feelings for her were.

He was already the champion of the oppressed, Alida told me, laughing: when his mother handed coins to the beggars outside the church, he always insisted she give that day's beggar a little bit more; she would shush him brusquely, reminding him that she had five children in the house and only one salary coming in, but he insisted, undaunted, until one or other of them gave in out of sheer exhaustion. One autumn day, Aunt Maria had seen him walk past a poor fellow who was huddled against a wall, wearing rags which were far too light for the weather; after a moment's hesitation, he had turned back, pulled off his sweater and given it to the man without saying a word. He hadn't noticed his sister, who was in a street at a point further up the hill, half-hidden by a low wall. When he got back home their mother had asked: 'And your sweater?'

'I lost it.'

'What do you mean, you've lost it?'

He had shrugged, and Maria had turned away to hide her smile. She never told him she had witnessed the scene.

He wasn't yet the reprobate son, though; or rather, these already slightly alarming eccentricities weren't yet seen as presages of future perdition. And in the photos Alida sent me after our phone call, the photos of her parents' wedding, with his puckish face, his cheeks unmistakably pink even in black-and-white, his jacket and tie, his hair combed back with pomade, the adolescent L.B. did not have the air I had imagined he would of being out of place among all the others, but quite the reverse: he was cheerful and at his ease. His posture and his laugh and his expressions were those of someone who is in the company of those he belongs with, people who speak the same language as him. Not like my mother as a child, who in all the photos with her family seems branded with an indelible mark of difference, of solitude, which is hard to explain but as conspicuous as a birthmark. Dora told me that, standing near the door of his old home, he had said: 'We were happy.' And why would he have been lying, at that point?

At the funeral of one of my uncles, the eldest, who died two years after L.B., Dora had met a woman from Monte Sant'Angelo who remembered him very well – 'the one with the head on him', the one who had managed to leave. When he came back down from Rome in the summer, he always dropped by, even though his family no longer lived in the town and hadn't for many years; and his arrival was welcomed with great excitement: he brought the latest news on the dance front, and singles with new hits that were all the rage at the fashionable Piper Club in Rome. So a record player was brought out into the piazza and they had open-air parties at which those eighteen-year-olds from the mountains spent hours dancing *il* twist, *il* surf and *lo* shake in a collective flutter of hair and maxi skirts and upraised arms, late into the night; and L.B. was at the centre of the circle, as always, moving from one partner to the next, and pirouetting and stamping his feet and clapping, and slowly, summer after summer, without any of the others noticing, dancing his way out of the centre of that circle and gradually slipping away, until, like a Fata Morgana, he disappeared over the horizon.

All the rest of it I'll never know. I will never know when it was that he first discovered books, or if he had a secret hideaway where he could daydream and read undisturbed, or what he knew about everything that lay beyond their mountain, and if he dreamed of seeing America or the jungle, or who his first love was and his best friend, or who he was with when he scampered along the '*passi riponte*', or if he had a special teacher, one of those teachers who can change the course of a life, or what he talked about with his brothers and sisters, what hurt him and what gave him joy, what legends and sirens lived in his head, what manner of things gave him that violent thrill which we only ever feel – quite so intensely – as children under twelve or thirteen, and how he came to fall madly in love with Ancient Greek, and why he decided to forget certain things. Or what it was, in the end, that made him different from all the others, all those generations of acquiescent and affably fatalistic people, the dutiful employees, the implacable housewives. Perhaps he grew to be like that, or perhaps he was already that way from birth, as if something in the bloodline had mutated. Where did that commanding, inexorable sense of justice come from? Was it a form of reaction, or pure fluke, or a calling?

How does a man come to be destined for compassion, for that burning pity Marguerite Yourcenar describes in her great-uncle Octave Pirmez: how does one come to be granted 'the horrible gift of looking at the world full in the face and seeing it as it is'?

III

SHELL

In the great dust cloud that was the year 1976, when the various groups disbanded one by one, and people who belonged to the old guard were left bewildered and adrift, exiled from the thing that had been their whole life, and many of them retreated from the battlefield tired and dispirited; in that year when words, faces and gestures all grew grimmer and some of the protests morphed into coldly plotted military sorties, and the Factory silently launched the 'restructuring', and any hope of there being a political project crumbled; in that dust cloud of things shattered, finished, cryptic and unsaid, that dust cloud suspended in a mysterious calm, or whipped up, at times, by equally mysterious and febrile moments of ferment, the figure of L.B. and the timeline of his existence become increasingly evanescent, as if merging, once and for all, into the backdrop of the city.

When he and Agata came back to live in Turin at the end of '75, L.B. decided to go back to practising medicine and he got a job at the hospital, at the Ospedale Molinette, very probably at the *Istituto di Anatomia e Istologia Patologica* where he had worked before Strada delle Cacce. All of this part of his life remains shrouded in mystery. L.B. disappeared, or he appeared to disappear, from the scene; but he also disappeared, after a fashion, from his life with Agata, who saw less and less of him. In what free time she had after work, she got involved in the feminist groups; he continued, before or after his shifts at the hospital, doing politics out and about, and they saw and spoke to one another very little. What it must have been like for that young woman who was not much more than a teenager, and whether or not she ever felt trapped, whether the solitude was painful or she felt resentful or jealous, the adult version of that woman never told me; and certainly not out of any residual conjugal deference, but because her loyalty towards L.B. was undimmed – that fraternal loyalty which I had noticed in her right from our very first meeting; the desire – still – to protect him. And perhaps L.B. felt he had done wrong by her, and, as in all his relationships, the guiltier he felt the more he ran away.

They were living, therefore, two separate lives which only rarely came briefly into contact. It may be that they fell in love with other people, and perhaps they changed imperceptibly as one does change at twenty and at thirty (a new shadow crossing your forehead, a new way of screwing up your mouth, a new deep and secret flaw in your character), without the other noticing. More and more like siblings, less and less like husband and wife. Agata was so young, he was already so aloof. That wasn't a marriage, Agata once said to me, with an indulgent laugh and that faraway look she had sometimes. It was a botch job arranged by other people, a relationship that might have lasted a few months if the party hadn't got involved. The true love of her life would be someone else, the man who came along many years later. But odd though their love story was, they always came back to one another in the end.

Here and there, though, a few sightings of L.B. were registered during the dust-cloud year. There are those who remember seeing him – bouncing around just like always and with that unmistakably joyful smile – walking alongside the furloughed workers, the metalworkers, the unemployed and the homeless, who marched through the streets of the city day after day. There are those who heard him give speeches at occupied factories, and at the university assemblies where his name was pronounced with the respect one reserves for the important ('We absolutely have to be there, *Barone*'s going to be talking,' said, in reverent tones, a classmate of Agata's future husband – who was still at high school and had never heard of him). And then there was Beniamino, known as Mino, a Sicilian lad with corkscrew curls, big glasses and the gift of the gab, who had arrived in Turin just one year earlier, at seventeen, and had already been laid off, with no unemployment insurance payments made, by the family friend who had so very kindly hired him; Mino had got involved in the *disoccupati organizzati* – the self-organising unions of the unemployed – ('We were definitely unemployed, but I'm not sure how organised we were,' he would tell me over forty years later, on the terrace of his home), and he remembers L.B. turning up at the university canteen with his big beard and his leather doctor's bag, and paying for the lunches of anyone who was out of work, and arguing with someone from the ICP, and then hurrying off.

Was all of this still in '76? Or was it already 1977 – the year which brought to a close the brief and hope-filled season of the 'young proletarians' circles', the year in which the destinies of Misa and Ester would first cross paths with that of L.B., and tragedy would put a match to so many other destinies? Or does one of these images belong to a later year? When the people who spoke to me tried to remember, the dates, as they always do, overlapped. The details were lost in memories of events too remote. In the ill-matched collision between individual biographies and history in general, dates and detail usually do belong only to the dead and the famous. Or murderers.

On 11 March 1977, in Bologna, during a protest against an assembly being held by *Comunione e Liberazione* at the *Istituto di Anatomia Umana*, the dean called the police. They arrived in large numbers and fired tear gas at the demonstrators, who were forced to retreat. As thick smoke invaded the streets and floated up towards the rooftops, some of them managed to make their way into roads the police were in, and threw granite cobblestones at them, and two Molotov cocktails. One of these hit the canvas roof of a personnel carrier, starting a small fire which was immediately put out. But the carabinieri conscript who was driving the personnel carrier pulled out his Beretta, or maybe a Winchester rifle, and advanced, firing twice, or maybe a dozen times, and then, reaching the corner of another street, firing directly into the crowd of protesters. One student was hit in the chest, dragged himself along for a couple of yards and then died. For two days the city blazed with a livid fury, with brutally violent baton charges

197

and barricades. Until the tanks sent by the government entered the by now deserted university district, and a bitter and deathly silence filled the streets.

On 12 March, at seven forty in the morning, in Via Gorizia, at the corner with Via Barletta in the Santa Rita quarter of Turin, a police brigadier in his early thirties with his hair neatly parted to one side left his house and went to get his canary yellow car. The brigadier in his early thirties had nothing striking to him, no particular guilt to expiate. His only peculiarity was that of being known to the people who were waiting for him; because he had been assigned to security duty outside the Faculty of Architecture and a couple of high schools, including the Galileo Ferraris science lyceum. And he often hung around outside, seraphically conferring, intervening in the clashes between left-wing students and right-wing students and calming the waters, and everyone treated him with the friendly indifference one feels for a familiar and inoffensive feature of the landscape, or even with a vague respect, because they knew that he didn't approve of the other policemen's 'methods' in the slightest, and he had voiced his criticisms more than once. The thing is, the brigadier in his early thirties was, from this point of view, perhaps unusual, but that didn't matter. Because the only thing that did matter, as far as his fate was concerned, was the fact that the Galileo Ferraris lyceum was where one of the three people who went to kill him worked as the librarian – a handsome lantern-jawed young man with an aristocratic nose and romantic eyebrows. And another lad, the one who stole the car they got out of, was still a student there. The brigadier served a single purpose: payback. He was the counterweight in an imaginary set of scales. Although, in effect, he did also fulfil another, subtler function: like the other man – the first one – who had been killed in Milan in '76 at the end of a patient wait for an umpteenth neo-fascist attack. Which happened, of course. One evening, in Porta Vittoria, a neo-fascist attack squad had waited at the corner of two streets for a student worker who had taken part in the occupation of the vacant houses in Piazza Risorgimento. They had knifed him repeatedly, and the young lad had died three days later; and for the reprisal a councillor from the neo-fascist *Movimento Sociale* party had been picked – a man, like the brigadier, without any distinctive characteristics, who had very regular habits and kept very regular hours. The murder of the councillor and that of the brigadier were personal initiatives taken by one man, Erno Bellaria, who was one of the founders of Front Line. Bellaria wanted to create a tipping point, to 'get down to business', he said, to present the hesitant with the fait accompli of the fantasy fulfilled: and so here it is, the enemy's carcass. Do you not smell it? Do you not see its ideological perfection? He would inform the National Command only once the task had been accomplished, exactly as he had done the first time around. Bellaria shot the brigadier without distinctive characteristics in the head, just as the man was climbing into his car.

Later that day, the ANSA press agency received a phone call claiming responsibility.

'Good afternoon. This morning's execution of the carabiniere was carried out by the Fighting Brigades. Please be careful to avoid confusing us with comparable organisations such as the Red Brigades.'

'But it wasn't a carabiniere.'

'Yes, it's that Security Service officer.'

'No, not the S.d.S. He was just political security branch, not intelligence.'

'We understand otherwise. And anyway, it's still a class enemy we're talking about.'

'OK, I hear you.'

'A communiqué is on its way. Write it down properly, the Fighting Brigades.'

'The communiqué, on its way when?'

'Sometime today.'

'All right. Look, make sure it gets dropped off somewhere near the office, that way there's less risk of it getting lost, which has happened on other occasions.'

'OK, thanks.'

'Good afternoon.'

Ah, what a magnificent sample of the extraordinary and transversal imbecility of the bureaucratic animal and of the lifeless language it speaks! And the dreary inventory of corpses and of communiqués sent by return had only just begun.

The murder of the brigadier without distinguishing characteristics was the first one in Turin. For a very long time there would be no others, and the episode was so unheard of, as was the name of the unknown group who claimed responsibility for it, that it quickly slipped to the back of people's minds. None of them ever imagined.

There were more pressing worries: the Red Brigades' leaders had to be put on trial, and it was continually postponed because the accused did not recognise the authority of the state judiciary and refused to be represented by court-appointed lawyers. And then, one rainy afternoon in April, the old *Avvocato* Croce who had been entrusted with the defence was murdered at the entrance to his office, and suddenly hundreds of defence lawyers and members of the public who had been called up for jury service fell ill, all of them with 'depressive syndrome'. The city was electric, dumbfounded, grim. A few weeks later, in May, arrests were made for a series of attempted bombings, armed robberies and violent assaults committed over the previous months. The arrested included Erno Bellaria and others from Front Line, and the party's Turin section was left without leaders. Hurriedly replacing Bellaria, and initially commuting back and forth from Milan, was a thin man with dark wavy hair, black eyebrows and round metal glasses, a man who looked shy and severe, like a youthful high-school philosophy teacher. In actual fact, he was one of the most expert of them from a military point of view, having been a drill instructor during his national service. He found himself faced with squads of students who were less competent than their Milanese counterparts, and a broken network of contacts with the Movement which needed to be reconstructed from scratch after the Turin section was almost entirely wiped out. The dramatic turn of events demanded urgency: he might as well give them military training.

The first operations were, all of them, messy and unsuccessful. In September, once the initial wave of detentions, searches, escapes and arrests was over, he decided that the situation required a firmer hand, and he moved to Turin, setting himself up in furnished accommodation in Corso Duca degli Abruzzi together with his girlfriend, with her pretty, sylvan name and tiny, dainty face. She would deal with all the logistical preparations for the murders, bombings and kneecappings. He was only twenty-four years old. He was a factory worker who was also enrolled at the university and, in the role of lookout, he had already participated in the killing of the neo-fascist councillor. His name was Mure Galiani.

Then came Misa and Ester's turn. It was almost summer by then, even though they had been the very first people I called, almost immediately. I think it might even have been the same evening I read the notice of appeal, back in that late December which felt like it belonged to another era now. My mother had suggested it, and I had hesitated for a moment; I had stood there, frozen, and looked at her, blinking very hard as if clutching at an idea, because I had forgotten that they had ever been part of my father's life.

'They were his friends at the time it all happened,' she had said. 'They were his best friends.'

When I phoned, it was Misa who answered; and – as I have already mentioned – he was left momentarily speechless when I told him what I wanted. And then, in a tone of voice I had never heard him use, very serious, sorrowful, almost grave, he had said yes.

They no longer lived in the flat in Parella (and hadn't for many years) where I had spent dozens of my childhood and teenage evenings. The flat with the big balcony looking on to a courtyard, the balcony where, in the summer, they and my mother used to sit and talk around a long, narrow table, and an ineffectual light bulb, hanging above them, used to buzz and flicker, reflected in the lenses of my mother's big glasses and on Misa's creamy skin and handsome Andean-looking features, and on Ester's aristocratic profile, which was sweet but also sharp, and their voices used to thrum reassuringly and there was a smell of mosquito coils and damp stone that came up from the courtyard, and I fell asleep in Misa's arms or knotted around the long legs and long apple-smooth arms of Altea, their daughter. Then they had gone to live in the countryside, and so had Altea, who had got married and had two very blonde little girls who must have emerged from some lovely hyperborean dream.

As a result, we had to wait a long time before meeting up, in order to combine one of my trips over from Milan and them being in the city; and so, there we finally were, at the old walnut table in my old home, Misa sitting to my left, Ester in front of me. Despite everything that had happened, they had come. They had come even though their long friendship with my father had come to an abrupt end when I was three years old and my parents had separated. Because, I vaguely sensed, of the way he had treated my mother, and, to a certain extent, me. Of the two, they had chosen my mother, even though they had only got to know her after I was born. From then on, they would only ever see my father at supper on Christmas Eve – which in our house is the only proper Christmas meal and has always involved a fixed group of ten or so friends (and the odd spare who happened to find themselves alone). My father prepared exquisite and unrepeatable plates of fish for everyone, with that astonishing grace he always brought to his cooking; and the guests paid him profuse compliments, but his part in the conversation never went any further than these polite exchanges of pleasantries.

For a very long time I had been entirely unaware of the fact that between Misa, Ester and my father there had been such a serious rift and such an important friendship, although at a certain point I had begun to sense the coolness and awkwardness between them, and it upset me terribly. I felt torn between two equally powerful affections; and I had a feeling that this meant I was being disloyal to my father – who, moreover, did nothing to make himself more appealing when they were around. It wasn't, I think, until I was a teenager that I learned he had been a friend of theirs, for over a decade. I was surprised, obviously – chiefly because they were so extraordinarily different from the friends he had now, and from what he had become – but I never asked any questions. Every now and then my father would ask sardonically how they were. They never talked about him. The day he died, though, on that muggy afternoon when I found myself in the hospital room and had sat down unthinkingly on a chair and no one had even glanced at me, all of a sudden Misa had appeared; he had burst into the room and we had thrown ourselves into one another's arms and had dissolved into tears in unison. Finally, one of *my people* had arrived. And then, pulling away from me, with a devastated look on his face, Misa had stammered: 'I will only remember the lovely things about your father, the bad stuff's all in the past,' and I had nodded dazedly and had sunk back into the safety of his arms.

Yes, they could emphatically be counted among the people who no longer loved my father. But they had come: and I saw instantly that they were feeling very emotional. And more than that: they were *happy*. What mysterious creatures humans are! L.B. – their L.B. – should by rights have been long forgotten, erased by the passing of time and by bitterness and disaffection. But instead, there he was.

This is what they told me. They told me about how the two of them – Misa and Ester – had known one another since they were little children, because they both came from the same village in the Val di Susa, and that they had got together when they were still in high school – a lifelong love, a love foreordained. And then later on, in Turin, when she was still studying at the specialist high school for future primary school teachers and he was enrolling in a teaching degree (after which he would go on to become a factory worker and eventually work for the electricity board), they had frequented the circles associated with Ongoing Struggle and Workers' Autonomy. Misa, who hadn't yet grown a beard, was baby-faced; Ester wore her hair straight, like a length of silk almost reaching her waist – the way she would keep it until I was four or five, when she cut it all off definitively. I still remember that chestnut curtain undulating like a restful sea every time she bent over to photograph something or to read.

After the disbanding of the groups, they, like many people, had flirted with the autonomist movement, dabbling in all the odd, inchoate, liberated stuff which was beginning to emerge at the time – and would quickly melt away: in Via Plana, the

Barabba club welcomed pretty much anyone who dropped by – 'Metropolitan Indians', young veterans of the disbanded groups, a hotchpotch of different people itching for something new and needing something else in life to be important, as well as politics. Sure, politics was still the most important thing; but there were so many aspirations and words flying around: about making space for human relationships, for bodies, for heterodoxy, for all the 'non-Marxist' art and cinema and literature they had overlooked for years; about looking in other directions, noticing the shape of a mountain or a cathedral, or a curious detail on the vaulted ceiling of an entrance corridor, or on an insect, or on a bird, or in an avenue in the autumn – being not just committed, but *alive*. We want poems! wrote three youngsters, in a letter to Ongoing Struggle's *Lotta Continua* newspaper that June. We've had it up to here with all the stultifying pamphlets and the meetings and the professional speechifiers. We want poetry, all the poetry available, all over the place, all over the walls, and all the better if it's the adolescent keening of some heartbroken teenage girl and not the tearful confession of the umpteenth leader at the umpteenth conference disbanding the umpteenth party; we want poetry even about polluted sunsets, we want bad poems too. We want them, even with all this ugliness and bleakness. And perhaps that's exactly why we want them.

Because that spring and summer were hard and ugly, peppered with murdered protesters and policemen, and men they shot in the legs, pulverising tibias cartilage kneecaps pelvises. Peppered with outlawed demonstrations and with neo-fascist ambuscades; and the political machine was becoming steadily more inept, more insular and cruel.

When was it that Misa and Ester first met L.B.? They were not quite sure. That year they were living with a group of friends, who just like them were all very young. Among the countless people coming and going there was this girl: a former schoolmate of one of their housemates, a gentle, charming, intelligent girl with long blond hair and a wispy fringe which fell into her eyes, a girl always dressed in baggy sweaters and shapeless jeans; her name was Petra and she worked at the Factory. It was with her and one of her colleagues that they first went along to the centre. The centre took its name from its location – Via Plava, in Mirafiori Sud, a redbrick building with a Scandinavian-style gable roof – and it welcomed in a good slice of Turin's autonomist workers' movement, people who weren't members of political parties and didn't belong to trade unions, and wanted to remain independent. And there in the middle of it all, having got there who knows how, was L.B.

So he continued turning up like this, as if by magic, always as unpredictable as a cat, always enveloped in a strange remoteness, even his powerful physical presence, even his sonorous voice. And he still possessed that mysterious incandescence which drew people to him, and that extraordinary concern for them all.

'If it's leaders we're talking about, that's not what he was,' said Ester, fidgeting with her rings. 'The most prominent people in the group were two others, a man and a woman. But somehow he was the one directing everything. He was far and away the most intelligent, out of all of us. He was the one who launched the debates by outlining a particular situation with a string of data, suggesting interpretations, summarising it all. He had an extraordinary ability to grasp the wider point, whatever the latest argument was, the ability to *see* things ... I don't know quite how to explain it to you. He had a sense of perspective. To be honest, I can barely remember what we said in those meetings, but we did talk, for example, about what was going on at the Factory, and he read the signs, he could see what was going to happen. Even if then, in '78, they took on thousands of people all in one go and he seemed to have got it completely wrong. But instead, it turned out he was right.'

'Are there any transcripts, of one of his speeches?' I asked, anticipating disappointment.

Misa and Ester exchanged a rueful smile.

'Nothing was ever written down, we just talked. At most, we put together a few scribbled reflections, afterwards. But it's impossible to say which ideas were his or someone else's. Or everyone's, collectively.'

They were only able to give me a generic description of what went on at the workers' centre in Via Plava; discussions were – naturally – had about what was happening right then in the city, and above all in the factories, and in the rest of the world; reading groups were formed to study non-orthodox texts. Like Vygotsky, for example, or McLuhan, and even writings leaking out of the prisons, things by political prisoners, which were then described to the committee and discussed together. They analysed the trialling of the automation of manual work and what the implications might be, whether they would be purely negative or whether there might also be some compensatory gains; they talked about life on the city's margins, about schooling, about the mounting repression.

Misa and Ester brought me an entire bagful of leaflets and booklets from those years, which I dipped into sporadically over the following months. I wasn't looking for anything in particular; I was just trying to clear a path for myself through all those convoluted words and references (which often escaped me). And the blows of my scythe occasionally dislodged enough dead leaves to reveal an interesting page or one that was slightly more comprehensible, especially when it came to research into prisons and the '*braccetti*' – the special maximum-security wings where the terrorists were held. And then one day – as usual, quite randomly – I found myself holding a typewritten document, its pages carefully numbered. From the very first lines – and the back of my eyes suddenly felt very hot – I instantly recognised my father's rococo style, the 'vernal breeze' blowing through a metropolis 'scoured by the frigid winds of the canons of power'. After all those years – and this would be the one and only time it happened – I was holding words belonging to L.B., words which were his and his alone, words which spoke to me, unmediated by others, of what he was thinking back then, of that brilliant, elusive mind. His own living words which finally, finally materialised, materialised physically on seven crudely stapled sheets of faded paper.

I read on. It may not have been signed, but yes, that piece was unmistakably his, from the very first line to the very last. It spoke of the need to recognise the linguistic plurality generated by the collapse of the extra-parliamentary leftist groups, breaking free from the old ideological frameworks and embracing new forms of knowledge. He talked at length about the importance of emancipating the human body, about the 'first strange reactions' emerging from the social maze 'in bodies which are increasingly unschooled'. Quoting another text which talked about the cleaving of body and psyche engendered by the capitalist society, and about the monstrous and alienated headless bodies and bodiless heads roaming the metropolitan landscape, he wrote: 'One's mind briefly skips back to the past; it revisits the dark places which were deeply introjected into every militant communist, and what re-emerges there is the system of absolute certainties represented by the Party-as-Truth. A chill ripples down one's spine, because for a very long time very many of us, especially those of us who adhered to Marxist-Leninism, were HEADS WITHOUT BODIES.'

I paused there, overcome by a rush of pity. I wondered which of the others, in that group of people who were nearly all of them at least five years younger than him, could have known those *dark places*. That pain was his own, that shame was his own. After all my searching and trying so hard to imagine, there it was: now I knew what Serve the People had meant to him. And there were lots of other deeply significant phrases: 'the magical name used for invoking the transition to communism' ... 'the tragic historical remnants of Marxism's fossilised ossification' ... 'a clear-eyed critique has to be made of our yellowing family albums' ... The document was undated, but it must have been from the early eighties, before they arrested him. It occurred to me that centuries, somehow, separated the young man making political speeches outside the university in Rome and the man who had written those things, the man who, in the novel 'strange reactions' of unschooled and emancipated bodies, had glimpsed a chance to shake off the vacuous solipsism of the headless bodies of post-everything-ism ('well, it's all in ruins now anyway, isn't it?'), the vacuous solipsism of you-have-some-fun-and-don't-think-too-hard, the vacuous solipsism which left the power structure definitively intact and unchallenged. A chance to create an opening for individuals, for specificities, for experiments – in contrast with that power structure which instead rendered people abstract and erased singularities, lumping everyone together (exactly like – he commented sarcastically – the grand ideology of the Party-as-Guide). They had to be saved, those human beings, and be transformed into bodies-with-heads; reality had to be severalised; its voices, its 'sounds', its 'micro-fractures' had to be listened to; people had to be rescued from the hegemonic codes which transformed individuality into *their* version of it: gratification, emulation, subservience-rewarded, blind adherence to the company mission, 'being "active" protagonists'. All things which, 'cut through, damn it. They work,' he wrote bitterly. It might perhaps prove impossible to find a chink in the wall via which to dialogue with that enemy hegemony, but – and this was the hope with which the document concluded – the abandoning of the Great Project, of one single key for decoding reality, and instead seeking diverse keys, diverse projects, a profusion of languages and forms of knowledge ... therein lay the most stimulating and vibrant of futures. There would be no more red dawn, but there would at least be a new language for a new existence.

And that was it. That was all there was. But I had already come to terms with the absurdity of a man having been politically active for all those years and in a period so seething with events and words, and nothing having survived apart from a few lines in some or other newspaper on the occasions when he was arrested. I had hunted for his name so many times – in the lists at the back of history essays or at the end of some newspaper article or among the contributors to a revolutionary pamphlet – and had never found it. So: this wasn't very much, but it was *something*. Now I was acquainted with at least a fragment of his political mind, and not just the sketchy aureole of other people's rememberings or disrememberings. I reread it over and over, studying its subtleties, its ingenuities, its insights. It existed, limpid and lucid: it was there for me. He surely never imagined that this would be the one thing his daughter would eventually track down, that it would remain her only physical record of his thinking, and he certainly wouldn't have remembered it, but there it was. And it was mine: because, in the heat of that long and gruelling hunt, amid hundreds of pieces of writing, I had, in a heartbeat, recognised this writing and known it was his.

When I went over to see them one day, in the kitchen of their house out in the countryside, Ester pulled on her venerable cat-eye glasses and, sitting at the table with dogs and cats prowling around us, showed me a pair of old family albums. Not their hundreds of photos of our holidays together when I was little, but the life from before. There were the holidays with L.B. and Agata. Greece, Puglia, ferries, faces I didn't know. A photograph of L.B. in shorts and sunglasses pushing Altea's buggy and, as he did so, laughingly saying something to Misa who was just behind him; the background seemed to be a town somewhere in the south. They were consistently cheerful images. And their albums, just like ours, had no real chronological order: the photographs were all mixed together, the dates jumped backwards and forwards. There were photos of their wedding, on 5 January 1978. Misa was twenty-three, Ester twenty-one. They were good looking. A photo of Misa, in very questionable red dungarees, holding a radiant and very rosy Altea in his arms; she was roughly two years old and dressed up in a carnival costume. A black-and-white photo of a teenage Ester surrounded by cousins; she must have been twelve or thirteen: she had a side parting and a herringbone-patterned jacket, and – already very tall – towered over the other children, her face awfully serious.

My thoughts returned to those photographs a few evenings later, back in Milan, while – true to form – stringing out my walk home after a meal out, and maundering through the dark streets between Piazzale Dateo and Corso XXII Marzo, and looking up at climbers lacing themselves around certain balconies where, like small domestic jungles, all kinds of plants spilled out, and there were apricot-coloured squares of brightness falling from windows with the lights left on. Those flash cards from the past materialising all of a sudden, the overly tall young girl who emerged from a group of cousins, the young man with the long hair and baby-face clutching his brightly dressed little girl ... They, together with so many others – my 'extended family' – had always been wholly part of my present tense: I had never asked myself what they had looked like beforehand, what hopes and dreams they had had, how their love stories had begun (or their current solitudes). I knew, because it was obvious, that they had once been young; I had, after all, even seen some of them – Misa and Ester, Nina, Teresa, my mother herself, and others – still young, not much over thirty, the age I myself was about to reach. But the way they were was a given, just as I had always been a given, I felt. And now, instead, it was as though they were suddenly reappearing to me.

I couldn't work out what that thought was supposed to mean. I tried breaking it down, looking at it from a different angle in the hope of feeling my way to an answer, but that didn't work. And yet I had the feeling of something having opened up, and of that something being connected in some strange way with the balcony-jungles and the light-filled windows. If I'd had to define that thought: somehow I was seeing more clearly. But it was still just an approximation. The answer to the riddle remained remote and inaccessible.

Then there was the great anti-repression protest meeting in Bologna. In September 1977. One hundred thousand of them went along, an entire movement of underground figures who wanted to emerge into the daylight, to show their faces and be seen by normal folk, to prove that not all 'autonomists' were the violent types they were made out to be. They had a lot to get through: the plan was to identify a common project linking all those people with so many very different stories behind them, to achieve a form of renewal, to 'question and confront', and, potentially, to set up a coordinating body for the 'organised avant-gardes'. As one enthusiastic worker from Piombino wrote in a letter to *Lotta Continua* on the day the meeting convened, 'I can hear even the old workers' locomotive creaking (might it be *rigor mortis*?).' Almost all of the impassioned letters, from men and women alike, explained that they were going to Bologna because they wanted to see and to understand.

It was a disaster. While the city filled with theatrical performances and parties and concerts, at the enormous gathering at the indoor sports arena the Movement's various 'spirits' clashed viciously. It emerged that in order to *do* something it wasn't sufficient to identify oneself as being *against* something; and that all of those 'spirits' were angry, insecure and confused, and reduced to chasing their tails in an eternally circular present tense, incapable of planning, imagining or proposing; and so they scuffled or patted themselves on their backs, and meanwhile, amid all the pointless and deafening chatter, the *armati*, the armed ones (that was how Misa and Ester referred to the terrorists; when they talked about the Movement, they called them the *armati* and the *non-armati*, the armed ones and the unarmed ones, unthinkingly using the jargon of the period, even now), the terrorists, prowled the debates discreetly, sniffing the wind to see if it might by any chance be blowing in their favour. They talked and talked and talked and talked, did the Movement's many 'spirits', for three whole days, and in the end they said nothing. Those who had come along hoping to see and to understand understood nothing, and witnessed only parties and singing and the motley dance of protest marches: as Andrei Bely wrote, we often drink coffee with cream while hovering above the abyss.

And the abyss lay just around the corner, closer than any of them could ever have imagined; it was as though a torrential storm of symbols were pouring down, rushing into the days ahead. In Bologna, together with L.B., Misa, Ester and so many others, Cecilia Longoni had come along too – L.B.'s old friend, who had abandoned active politics a while back but wanted to be at the meeting all the same. On their way back home, sitting in front of her, his head leaning on the window of the train, he had said to her: 'It's all over.'

Cecilia didn't ask what. He closed his eyes and said nothing more.

The meeting in Bologna drew to a close on 25 September. A heartbeat later, in Rome, within the space of three days the neo-fascist Armed Revolutionary Nuclei shot two lads, who happened to be sitting on a bench, and a girl, who would spend years in a coma before dying – first the lads, then her, methodically, implacably, in goose-step; and then finally, on 30 September, Walter Rossi, who was twenty years old, was shot fatally in the neck while he was out protesting about the wounding of the girl.

And then, on 1 October, Roberto Crescenzio went up in flames.

One day, when I would have been ten or eleven years old, my father and I were queueing outside a cinema in Via Po. We often went to the cinema together. Out of the blue, nodding in the direction of the bar next door, he said: 'You know, that bar used to be called the Blue Angel.'

He paused.

'A young man burned to death in there,' he added. 'They threw some petrol bombs in ... during a protest. He took fright and shut himself in the toilet. And then he burned to death.'

I looked up at him, trying to interpret the expression on his face, but it was unreadable. I don't remember whether or not I asked him why they had thrown the bombs. I found it astonishing that he would think to tell me, and do it the way he did, as a bolt from the blue. The story went no further and we reached the smiling ticket seller, and that was that, and then we went into the cinema and I was distracted by other things. But that conversation was one I had always remembered, because of the subtle feeling of unease it left me with, because of the way his voice had throbbed, and because of the casualness of that horrific anecdote. He had never said anything to me about other places where people had been killed, or about other episodes; which meant that, for him, the Blue Angel was a thing so repugnant, so inconceivable that he had found himself telling even me about it: and I still hadn't even started middle school. I couldn't help thinking about it whenever I walked past there, even though we never spoke of it again. The Blue Angel became part of that category of words which I will forever associate with a subterranean and suffocating uneasiness, like W. W. Jacobs' monkey's paw; those names which, every time you hear them, sound just like Peter Lorre whistling in Fritz Lang's *M*. But this wasn't imaginary, it was real, and it was *proximate*: perhaps that was why it upset me so very much.

I would only read about the events at the Blue Angel fifteen years later: the march organised on 1 October to protest against Walter Rossi's death; the furious column of marchers looking for targets for their rage; the tension so palpable that they could hardly breathe. Unable to attack the local headquarters of the neo-fascist *Movimento Sociale Italiano*, which was under police guard, the procession veered off towards Via Po. There, at the end of the road, just a block away from Piazza Vittorio, stood that bar, the Blue Angel, which was rumoured to be the haunt of heroin dealers and fascists. Heroin as a substitute enemy? That would do fine. Roberto Crescenzio was also in the bar that morning – a student worker (a proletarian, the editorials in *Lotta Continua* and the other communist newspapers would howl despairingly in the days that followed; we have killed a proletarian, a proletarian!). He was having a drink with a friend. When the guys in balaclavas arrived, they shouted at the barman and clients to get out – which was standard practice. Perhaps Roberto Crescenzio was already in the toilet. Perhaps fear made him move irrationally, and he went the wrong way and locked the door behind him. The petrol bombs were thrown. The Blue Angel burst into flames.

Outside, people stopped to watch the crackling conflagration. Then it happened. At a certain point, as though out of the gates of hell, a figure emerged. It was a creature from the depths of nightmares. It was entirely black. It had no clothes, just scraps of fabric dangling from it. It had no hair. It had no face. It was just a carbonised body and it was tottering forward with its eyes agape. Everyone fell silent. Where had it come from? What was it, that thing? They starred at it, horror-struck. Someone managed to think rationally for a second, and brought over a chair from God knows where. The body sat down. There are photos still in existence of the creature on that chair, surrounded by people with their arms hanging limply by their sides. Then the body was taken off to hospital. The chair was left there, near the porticoes, for hours, too dreadful to be touched, with the charred remains of the clothes lying next to it and, on its seat, the black mark left where the body had sat.

During the night between 2 and 3 October, on one of the walls in Corso Valdocco someone wrote 'It's not a good moment', in red paint. A crushing silence filled the city.

Crescenzio survived, lucid for almost all of it, for too many days – two – and then surrendered himself to a merciful death.

The Blue Angel would remain a gaping and irreparable wound in the history of Turin. Everyone who remembers it happening talks about it with shame, even if they weren't there that day. One way or another, all of us are responsible, they wrote – after Roberto Crescenzio's death. They had crossed a threshold from which no one could turn back innocent or pure or free like children are free. The Blue Angel was quite literally the unspeakable crashing down on them and hooking itself into their flesh for ever. That day marked the definitive rupture between those who decided to abandon politics because they couldn't bear the idea that their world had produced that creature from hell, those who stayed on and, with growing desperation, tried to pick up the pieces, and those who, in the end, chose the armed struggle, which in this case meant Front Line, because as things stood there was nothing else left, was there? All of the circuits had been broken, the groups no longer existed, the Red Brigades were so remote they were almost lunar, the State crushed without making subtle distinctions. At least there, in Front Line, there were squads, some semblance of organisation (Mure Galiani was planning to create a proletarian militia), the seductive splendour of action. Roberto Crescenzio became a symbol. And I find myself thinking how atrocious it is that a person, that any human being, should be fated to be a symbol, and that Roberto Crescenzio had a body of his own, and a brain, and an anonymous and normal life, and instead he had to become the mangled carcass at the fork in someone else's road, a poor martyr who had no desire to be one, the monster in the photos, the culpability of an entire city. We often talk about the tragedy of an individual, or of a multitude, as being of service in exposing the deplorable scandal of a particular deed or practice: I always wonder what that individual or multitude would have to say. And I think how much implicit horror there is in an affirmation of that kind, however well-intentioned. No, the burning of Roberto Crescenzio served no useful purpose, it symbolised nothing: I won't accept it.

The Barabba club, which had already been kicked out of the premises in Via Plana because the city council wanted to build a nursery school there (the school I would attend just over ten years later, by yet another strange trick of fate), crumbled into the up-rushing waves of that October. One of its leading lights – who was nicknamed Kim, like something out of one of Salgari's novels – joined the Front Line squads not long afterwards, going on to become a fugitive, head of the first city-centre patrol group and a member of Front Line's Turin command group. Opposing that choice, and opposing the idea of the armed struggle in general, another member of the club – Albertino, an enigmatic lad, charming and astute, with a tousled fringe of fine hair over a handsome face – wrote a blistering manifesto, of which many of them, decades later, still remember the conclusion: 'From here on in, you can make history without me.'

Late in the afternoon of one December day in 1977, the doorbell rang at the surgery of a fifty-year-old doctor who received patients in the Cit Turin quarter of the city, the art nouveau quarter with all the dragon- and lion-crowned architraves. A male voice exhorted: 'Open up, this is the police!'

The receptionist opened the door. Four people with their faces unmasked locked her in the lavatory, walked into the doctor's room, chased out his patient and then turned their attention to the man facing them, who made a feeble effort to defend himself but was kicked and punched and fell to the floor. The four – three men and a woman – employed a curious technique on their target. They tied him to the radiator by his wrists and subjected him to a brief 'proletarian trial'. Then they shot him using a 7.65mm pistol, reducing a shoulder and one of his knees to a pulp (the other knee survived because the pistol jammed). When they were done, they hung a cardboard sign around his neck: 'The proletariat does not forgive its torturers.'

Then off they vanished. The note claiming responsibility was apparently signed 'Armed Workers' Combat Squads'. The receptionist telephoned for help, the doctor was taken to the nearest hospital, and one reporter (the *Gazzetta del Popolo* had its offices right next door and reached the hospital at the same time as the injured party) noted that when they cut open his clothes and saw the bullet wounds, one of the medics whispered: 'Jesus Christ, they've crucified him!'

They asked the doctor who he was. He didn't answer; he turned his face to the wall. They asked him again, and again, and eventually he hissed: 'My name is Coda.'

For a second, everyone in the room stood still.

Villa Azzurra had an enchanting name. Villa Azure. It was the children's lunatic asylum. The diagnoses made were fairly questionable and hadn't been reviewed for years, but it didn't much matter: the patients came from illiterate or dirt-poor homes in which they had never mastered speech; or they were the children of unmarried women who didn't know what to do with them; or they were 'disturbed'. But an appropriate class of mental deficiency was always found for every case. They were tied to their beds for much of the time and the nuns washed them using scrubbing brushes. As certain little girls grew bigger they would often be taken off somewhere for a couple of hours by the male nurses. Those girls put on weight. They ate too many sweets, said the nuns. Then the girls would disappear.

One Christmas a film was screened; its title was *The Freedom of Zoos*.

Most of the time the children were so heavily drugged that they couldn't tell day from night. One of them routinely walked backwards. The more troublesome among them were caned or tied to the radiators.

The medical director was a man called Giorgio Coda.

His methods were interesting. The unruliest little boys were encouraged to let off steam by fighting like pit bulls, until they collapsed, wounded and exhausted; but his speciality, the reason he had been selected to run Villa Azzurra, was electroshock therapy. That was why he would forever be known as the Electrician. He called them electromassages: in particular, he punished masturbation, attaching electrodes to and inside the relevant body parts; but it was used to punish pretty much anything. Or simply because the fancy took him. There was one little boy, possibly the son of a prostitute, certainly the son of a poor woman, who had ended up in the adult asylum after swallowing a marble in a fit of pique – and then, given that it was *unthinkable* that he should be kept among the insane adults, he was moved to the children's asylum. His name was Albertino. He tried escaping over the rooftops, and when he was retrieved by his diligent gaolers – because there were many people within those walls, not just the Electrician, who were involved in applying the 'restraining measures' and all the rest of it – he said he simply couldn't help himself. He was tied up and subjected to electromassages, but it did no good, he didn't adapt, his light wasn't snuffed out like the others' were. He would eventually – still a child – be one of the key witnesses at the Electrician's trial. Later on, at the age of thirteen, he was adopted by a rich left-wing family who decided they would take care of that unhappy, sarcastic, incorrigible little escapee.

In July 1970, a photographer from the *Espresso* magazine managed to get into Villa Azzurra. He wandered through the wards without anyone noticing he was there. He photographed children who were tied up, covered in flies, expressionless; children who occasionally smiled toothlessly, indescribably, into the camera. He photographed a little girl whose name was Maria, and her portrait became the feature image for the report. Her hair was short, her face sweet, her body totally naked, and her wrists and ankles were bound, like a crucifixion. The scandal broke; the little ones were 'set free' in an absurdly haphazard manner, without over much attention being paid to where they ended up;

Maria, who had severe learning disabilities, died a few years later, drowning in the bath where she had been left unattended by the person who was supposed to be looking after her.

They wrote a book about the Electrician. It was one of the most egregious of the cases exposing what was going on in the fetid seclusion of the asylums. But despite being sentenced to five years' imprisonment, he remained at liberty – thanks to an amnesty and a legal loophole. Front Line went to get him knowing perfectly well who he was; and everyone in the Movement knew Albertino, the strange, handsome Albertino and his harrowing story. Even if he had vehemently disowned the armed struggle. The vendetta was a success. Mule Galiani was enthusiastic: as a piece of propaganda, the physical destruction but not murder of the Electrician was a well-thought-out operation on every level (it was very hard to feel compassion for a monster), and was almost universally well received. They had selected the ideal target: they were true champions of justice, finishing the job the State had failed to complete.

More than forty years after the 'reprisal' against the Electrician, I was reading a book about the children's asylums when I unexpectedly came across a name too unusual not to catch my eye. It was one of the little boys who had been at Villa Azzurra. That name started hammering away in my head. It was the name of a famous liberator of slaves (what a heartbreaking irony). The book noted that many of the survivors of Villa Azzurra proved unable to shake off what the institution had done to them, and had been looked after, from the late eighties onwards, by a cooperative I knew of. It was the one my father had worked in after he graduated in psychology. And I had very clear memories of the big burly man that the little boy named after the liberator of slaves had become. He had frightened me: because he was so tall, and because he always held his head boxed in between his shoulders, and his watery blue eyes were as empty as his face, and he spoke in fits and starts. My father had a soft spot for him: he pronounced that weighty name with great tenderness; he would repeat it, sometimes, in a sing-song lilt, as though he were trying to help him to sleep. And every once in a while S.'s shoulders relaxed.

'You smoke too much,' my father would say to him with a kindness which was almost loving. S. would rock backwards and forwards, and would offer him a vague smile which I had the impression was also loving.

I discovered that S. was still alive. I found a short documentary, made a year earlier, in which it was explained that, after the cooperative had flopped, he had been adopted by a family who now cared for him. He hadn't changed at all; his hair was just a bit whiter. He spoke about Villa Azzurra in the documentary. He remembered all of it – the scrubbing brushes, the sheets they wrapped and twisted around his head until they almost smothered him every time he had a fit. One boy had died in the bed next to his; he had been feeling bad for hours but no one had come to help, even though S. had reassured him: they'd be coming soon to look after him, they'll be here soon, you'll see.

That was one of the most devastating bits. I hadn't expected it. I wept for ages, thinking of S. and all the others, and the little ones who had been taken in and looked after, and the surprising way those stories interlaced. Albertino had died of AIDS a long time ago, still very young, having spent two and a half years in jail during the early eighties and having lived other lives. But the others, the genuinely insane or the ones who were driven insane by force of circumstance, had continued to drift around the suburbs in the vicinity of the abandoned asylum, occasionally venturing into the city centre, until the day someone opened a door which was hidden behind sprays of wisteria, and let them in. And eventually, from beneath that wisteria, L.B. also made his entrance.

Once, when I was talking to two of L.B.'s old comrades, one of the two – who had been a worker at the Factory and knew him well, and had then become a teacher, and also knew my mother well – had asked me: 'But how are you are planning to put this story together? Will you take it up to his death?'

He had drawn an arc with his hand in the air.

'No, it's not a biography. I'm not telling the story of his life afterwards, I'm just talking about those, let's say, fifteen years. It's the story of a man's downfall.'

His eyes had tightened.

'No, no. It was not a downfall.'

'But it's just a narrative arc, it's not a judgement,' I had explained patiently and patronisingly.

'No, because if the part after that is missing ... the part where your father went to look after the mad ... it's as though it's missing a bit, do you see? If he had fallen from grace, if he had *really* fallen from grace, he would have gone off to make himself some money!'

My other interlocutor nodded.

'You must understand, Marta, he didn't fail. He stayed there, right to the end. Right to the very end, with the people he was supposed to be with.'

I hadn't said anything in reply. It wasn't wrong, but it wasn't part of my story.

And instead, now, suddenly, he was right. It all flowed together in a perfectly coherent design. Albertino and Maria and the Electrician and S. the former child from Villa Azzurra, and the chilling shadow of Villa Azzurra which re-presented itself again and again like a sibilant background hum in nearly all of the books on that period, in the books I was reading as part of my research. That evening I thought about them repeatedly – about the little boy who swallowed a marble and spat on the armed struggle, about Maria being crucified and drowned, about the boy who walked backwards, about the boy I had unknowingly known as an adult, and about this unexpected link with my father. So, even the L.B. I'd never taken into account, the L.B. from *afterwards*, the L.B. who had been part of my life and whom I tended to think of as tired and shambolic, had continued his methodical, anonymous work, for ever and always in metaphorical opposition to the by then defunct Front Line and their 'revolutionary praxis' and their *prêt-à-porter* vendettas which saved no one, which helped no one, and certainly not those who, notwithstanding the Electrician and the system which produced him, had had no choice but to continue to exist. The city of the rejected. The hidden, embarrassing, wounded city whose suffering incited no outcry or '*geometrica potenza*' – no 'carefully computed firepower'. That piece of his life was not, therefore, a superfluous section; it was the return and evolution of a motif, one of the most important of them – if not the central leitmotif in his outlandish biography. Sometimes human life reveals an unexpected and admirable flair for counterpoint.

When Via Fani finally arrived, it took everyone by surprise. Everyone was knocked sideways, from Front Line to the unarmed elements of the autonomist movement; and the initial, hazy exaltation at an attack of that kind being launched on the very heart of Christian Democrat power rapidly gave way to total confusion. One friend of L.B.'s recalls that on the day the Christian Democrat former prime minister was kidnapped and his police escort butchered, or perhaps the day afterwards, he had gone round to her flat to pay her a visit, and had walked round and round the kitchen picking up random objects and putting them back down again, visibly agitated.

'He was *livid*,' she told me. 'I was still buzzing, and I said: "Leo, it's incredible, isn't it?" And he said grimly: "Oh, it's positively hilarious."'

And soon enough, in fact, a vortex would start forming, a vortex in which they would all be caught up, all destroyed. The ICP and the trade unions immediately broke off all relations with everything to the left of them, to avoid the risk of being labelled 'allies of the Red Brigades'. And as an inevitable consequence, everything to the left of them was automatically suspected of 'being in alliance'. Blanket arrests and searches began, indiscriminately targeting the entire autonomist 'area', regardless of the fact that the majority of the autonomist groups had dissociated themselves – with angry and even outraged editorials and press releases – from a trajectory they now considered wholly derailed.

In Front Line, nobody had the faintest idea what to do. But then again, after such an unexpected and inordinate gesture on the part of the Red Brigades, the ante had to be upped. It was unavoidable. Even if one of their unshakeable precepts, right from the start, had been that anyone who joined the organisation would always be free to leave at any time, that was now no longer possible. They were going to have to speed up the military training of members, and above all opt, inevitably, all of them, to go into hiding. Up to that point, in fact, most of them had continued to hold down normal jobs, clocking on and off and taking part in armed operations in their free time – the wage slaves of the armed struggle, some people called them – in order to keep in touch with the Movement, with social conditions and with the situation 'on the ground'. All of this had ended abruptly when the ex-prime minister's body had been bent in two in the boot of that car. The ex-prime minister's body, which had dropped like a tombstone on to the weak and equivocal theoretical vertebrae of the armed organisations. And all that was left was that terrible open plain, with no rocks at their backs, where all they could do was shoot, and shoot again, and shoot harder, and leave the field open for eighteen-year-old boys who dreamed of their own Via Fani, and for all manner of misfits – anything to guarantee that the ranks swelled, anything to let in torrents of arms. If beforehand it had just been reprisals, or malefactors being punished, now they were going to have to align themselves with the others, now they were going to have to blow everything up. Ideology included. Up to now the Red Brigades hadn't even been entirely sure what Front Line was; they were about to find out.

Wholescale arming. That was Mure Galiani's plan. 'Extending the use of arms and generalised hostilities to involve all social actors', from workers to students, who would thus be able to rise up against their individual masters. And so a new round of recruitment began in Turin. Other members of the party's command considered it sheer madness, above all the idea of putting weapons into the hands of youngsters, but they didn't succeed in stopping him. Front Line had embarked on a precipitous race towards ruin, and would leave behind them a long and bloody trail of tatters of human flesh.

'*Dans les rues de Turin-la-Terreur*'. *France Soir*'s headline, on 13 April 1978, above the front-page photograph of the corpse of the prison warder Lorenzo Cutugno. Spread across a pavement. Killed by the Red Brigades. In the streets of Turin-the-Terror. Villefranche-sur-Mer, Chalon-sur-Saône, Turin-la-Terreur. As though that were now the city's very name, the lurid essence of her soot-streaked pale yellow façades, of her balconied court-yards, of the melancholy cobbled back streets which by night shine only in patches with the light of infrequent streetlamps; the essence of the slow-moving river, of the huge blocks of flats out in the suburbs, of the indifferent statues and grand parks; as though death had seeped up and into all of this like water, until it was so saturated that its nature was irretrievably altered.

We can kill everyone, and we will kill everyone. From a certain point onward, that's what the narrative seemed to be.

Meanwhile, in the storm-tossed little barque of the committee as it battled to stay afloat in the middle of this murky squall, L.B. and the others continued, undeterred, to seek a route to change via everyday actions, without arriving at the extreme methods which he not only abhorred but also found useless. A baby had been born during that dark and stormy spring – the very young Petra had had a little girl. L.B. adored her and the baby reciprocated; whenever she saw him, she clapped her hands happily; once she started pronouncing her first words, she even nicknamed him 'papo' – dadda. But the wolves were gathering.

L.B. was arrested for subversive association as 'one of the leaders of the workers' autonomist movement in Turin', as the article in La Stampa on 16 May 1978 defined him, a few days after ex-Prime Minister Moro's body was found.

A friend of mine who worked in an archive sent me a short article he had come across – quite by chance, without knowing anything about what I was working on – which had appeared in Lotta Continua on 17 May and talked specifically about L.B. 'Turin is also seeing regular round-ups of "allies", a label which seems to be applied with increasing regularity to the movement's better-known and more combative elements. One such is, in fact,

Leonardo Barone, a comrade from the PCIM-L and a member of the standing committee on state repression, familiar to all comrades in Turin thanks to his assiduous and very public activism, and arrested yesterday morning during one of approximately thirty raids conducted by DIGOS special operatives and the carabinieri. In addition to Leonardo, those arrested included [...] The head of DIGOS, F.F., stated that the comrades are accused "of being responsible for episodes of violence during protest marches, although none of them have, however, been involved in attacks on individuals". This is an indirect confirmation of the deliberately inflammatory nature of these arrests, which follow police searches indiscriminately targeting comrades from '68, militants from Ongoing Struggle and trade union representatives. Leonardo Barone is guilty only of communism and, like the other comrades, must be freed immediately, and continue to fight alongside us.'

However deliberately inflammatory his arrest was or wasn't, L.B. was released a few weeks later, apart from anything else because there wasn't a single piece of evidence that he had ever committed any act of violence under any circumstances, or that he had ever been involved in any subversive association. Agata told me that there had been talk of putting him under an internal deportation order: the appointed destination, in a crowning absurdity, would have been Monte Sant'Angelo, the little town of his birth, up at the top of the mountain. Of all the arrests in L.B.'s large collection, this one would not have been particularly significant, had it not been – at least, as far as emerges from my laborious reconstruction – the second major turning point of his existence; in other words, the apparent reason for which he abandoned his job at the hospital. The story he had alluded to so hazily, the dates that didn't tie up, the fact that he had one day said to Dora, with whom he never talked about that period, that just before he was arrested he had been offered a research post at a clinic in Germany, and that this had perhaps been the motive for which his colleagues had, maybe not boycotted him, but certainly abandoned him in the face of the allegations and hadn't lifted a finger in his defence. So, was this the point at which L.B. went off to work at the factory, without telling anyone, even his wife or his closest friends? Was this the point when that happened? It could be that, having been charged with subversive association, he was banned from practising medicine: but once the charges were dropped, would he not have been able to return to his post? Or perhaps, at this point, he retreated into himself for a second time, incapable of juggling his too many lives? I will never know. It will always remain one of those blank spaces in his existence, one of those empty gaps to which no one has ever had access, and one of that unpredictable man's cussedly self-inflicted defeats.

It was then, therefore – or maybe earlier, who knows? – that L.B. went to work at Materferro, seizing the opportunity offered by the recruitment drive underway at the Factory which, in those months, was amassing a cache of tens of thousands of people. Materferro was the section of the plant dedicated to railway materials. It doesn't exist any more: nowadays there is just a deserted area fenced off behind partially uprooted railings, into which only weeds, tramps and rabbits ever trespass.

L.B.'s factory-worker period is another black hole. I haven't found a single informant who worked in the same section as him. Outside the factory, however, the Via Plava committee had in the meantime gradually transformed itself into an anti-repression committee; and one evening, Ester remembered, a couple had come along – two shy older people who owned a flower shop. Their son had been arrested for membership of an armed band. He was being held in one of those preternatural and still baffling entities known as super-maximum security prisons, and they brought news of torture allegedly taking place, or something equally terrible. (In yet another coincidence, or another one of life's clever thematic threads, one of the super-max prisons was in Trani.) Misa, Ester and others began travelling regularly to Milan, to the Leoncavallo social centre, where they were collating information emerging from the secure wings and piecing together the murkier details regarding detentions, and also the reports of torture, which, following the Moro kidnapping – or 'Operation Fritz', as the Red Brigades called it – was being used more frequently, although it has never been entirely clear to what extent. By now, this occupied all their energies. Relatives of the incarcerated comrades had joined the committee; they glossed over *what* the comrades had done; a prisoner is a prisoner – they thought – regardless, especially if they happen to be a comrade, and it was important to defend their right to decent living conditions wherever they were detained. They gathered together eyewitness reports. They wrote leaflets to spread the news. Their discussions all focused on the prisons question. There evidently wasn't much else they could do.

And there were lots of prisoners now, so many of them. The first time I went round to have supper with Sara and Mino – who had met during the infamous thirty-five-day strike at the Factory, and had been together ever since – at their flat with the big terrace from which you could see almost all of the city and where a skinny little ten-year-old was messing around, a daughter who had arrived late in life, a girl with a sharp, intelligent face ... Mino said to me, in a stream of words interrupted every so often by an equable comment from Sara, that there had come a point at which you never met anyone, any more, when you were out and about, because they had all been taken in. Mino was the Sicilian lad who had met L.B. when he was involved in the *disoccupati organizzati*; she, Sara, was a little bit older than him, a gentle woman with an expressive, vivacious face with lots of cheerful shrewdness in it, and her first encounters with L.B. had been at factory assemblies in the late seventies. They showed me a few photos of L.B. and of their holidays together. Mino was an enthusiastic photographer and some of the pictures were very lovely; his black-and-white photos of Berlin and other cities were really quite artistic. One of the photographs that Agata had given me had – I discovered, while watching my host scan a roll of negatives in search of my father's face – been taken by him: a close-up shot of L.B. lying on a bench during some holiday or other, his bearded face leaning on his hand, eyes closed, features relaxed, a quiet smile. Mino had managed to capture something you never saw in other pictures of him.

There was one photo I found particularly striking. It was a photograph of a picnic, a barbeque. L.B. was recognisable, on the left, lying on his front next to a young woman, and talking, with a smile, to a little girl who must have been a year old or thereabouts and was standing in front of him in her T-shirt and nappy. He had his elbows on the ground, his hands joined to form a pyramid, and his eyebrows arched as though what he was listening to was very interesting; Mino and Sara didn't remember who the little girl was, or who many of the other people at the picnic were. And there were lots of other people, sitting, lying down, standing near the barbeque. On the right-hand side of the photo you could no longer see the people who were standing up: time, or abrasion from boxes or from objects it had ended up sitting under, out of carelessness, at the bottom of some drawer, had decoloured their faces almost to the point of erasing them. All that was left was their shirts with the sleeves rolled up, and their legs, a few hands holding cigarettes, the shoes in the grass.

'These people,' said Mino, running his index finger over the part of the photo where the faces had vanished, 'all ended up taking part in the armed struggle.'

I looked at him and then looked back at the photo. It was staggering. I had never seen such a ludicrously symbolic real-life object; things like this belonged in books. That neat division between the redeemed and the unredeemed, between those who were lost to perdition and those who weren't: improbable though it was, that was entirely a product of chance. And so, by pure accident, that tattered little photograph had become the tragic effigy of an era.

Sara drove me back to my mother's house. It was gone midnight. When we came to a stop in the middle of the deserted street in front of my door, she turned round to look at me and said: 'Listen, there's something I wanted to say to you.'

'Yes.'

'If your father didn't become someone important, if he didn't become a party leader, it's because he chose not to. He had all the makings of a major political figure. But he didn't want it. He always preferred being in the rank and file. He didn't want to be a leader. Do you understand?'

I nodded.

She peered through the windscreen at the lights in our building's windows. 'I came round to see you all here, once. You were very tiny. It was snowing really hard; it took us hours to get here. But I remember the flat, and your mother. I would like to see her again, one of these days. Margherita ...'

She smiled at me. It felt like there was something shared and secret in that dark street with no one walking by, in the words she had kept back for the very last minute, in that nocturnal, tranquil city where there seemed to be only the two of us. I smiled at her too.

It is interesting to re-walk the route that led to L.B.'s brush with Mure Galiani; if nothing else, because almost all of the variables that can possibly determine the fate of a series of human beings can be seen in action: fluke, solitude, vendetta, stupidity, arrogance, mistaken identity, stubborn blindness.

It was February 1979. The city had recently lived through thirty-six terrorist attacks in under sixty days. In Milan, meanwhile, Judge Alessandrini had been killed by Front Line; and back in the autumn, in Naples, as part of the 'prisons campaign' against the emergency laws and the wretched conditions inside the jails, F.L. had also murdered Professor Paolella, a specialist in the anthropology of crime who was promoting prison reform and a series of other reforms intended to encourage the rehabilitation of offenders, and drug addicts in particular. Why target the 'righteous' (who, for that matter, included Alessandrini)? Well, because there was a terrible danger to be avoided: that these righteous men might render the institutions of government more palatable, that they might change them for the better and thus eliminate the putative need for organisations that sought to sweep the institutions of government away in a hail of revolver rounds. In January they had killed a prison warder in Turin. Thanks, in part, to the feverish competition between different armed groups, the ante had indisputably been upped. The ICP in Turin had decided to circulate a questionnaire, which was much criticised. In particular because of question 5: 'Are you in the possession of any concrete facts which might be of help to the judiciary and the forces of law and order in identifying individuals who commit terrorist attacks, robberies or assaults?' That meant grassing, as more than one person pointed out. And what if somebody were to incriminate somebody else purely for personal vendetta? But the neighbourhood committees were distributing the questionnaire all the same. The young president of the Borgo San Paolo and Madonna di Campagna committee began to suspect he was under surveillance: for days now, he had been seeing the same person walking along the pavement in front of his house. Then he noticed a car with four people in it hanging around until he caught his bus, and at the next stop a young woman would get on and sit down beside him and then get off at the same stop as him. Maybe it was just a coincidence, but he really was beginning to worry.

Scene one. On the morning of 28 February, in a tobacconist's, three young people asked if they could try on the carnival masks. Seeing as carnival had been a while back and this was the third time in three days that they had come into the shop, the tobacconist smelled a rat, imagining they wanted to use the masks for a robbery. As soon as they left, he called the police for a third time. That morning the police actually turned up. The three young people – two men and a woman – went into a nearby bar for a coffee. They had been there for less than five minutes when a police patrol walked in and asked to see their identity cards. The young people didn't say a word: they pulled out weapons and started shooting. The policemen returned fire. No one knows for sure how things unfolded that day, but when the gunfire finally fell silent, it was two of the three young people who lay dead on the floor of the bar: she had a now-worthless bullet-proof vest under her beige Loden coat, and thin eyebrows, and a beret pulled down over short, red curls. He looked remarkably young. The newspapers printed photos of their corpses, of their faces, which were not startled by death, but serious. Focused. Their clothes had been removed for no obvious motive, except, perhaps, as some sort of tribal message for other terrorists; their naked bodies were left abandoned on the floor. 'Greetings from Turin' said the headline in *Il Male*, above that terrible photo. Although the arsenal they were equipped with clearly pegged them as terrorists, the police took a while to work out who they were. Then Front Line sent over a statement in which honour was paid to 'Charlie and Carla'. His name was Matteo and he was a worker at the Factory's Rivalta plant. Twenty years old; still enrolled in year four at the scientific lyceum. He came from an already devastated family – a father doing life for mafia and homicide, two older brothers who had been in and out of jail – and when they went round to tell his mother, she started screaming that no that wasn't possible, not him too, this family is jinxed ... Matteo was one of the kids from the latest round of recruits. He had said to his friends, once, that death would be better than jail. Barbara, the woman, was twenty-nine and mother to a little girl. She had been a prominent communist militant in Bologna. She had been involved in all of the most important campaigns of that period. Before going into hiding as a member of Front Line together with her partner of several years, Bastien Vivaldi (the third man in this particular scene, the one who managed to escape), she had been a nursery school teacher.

Scene two. In Front Line they were all stunned: it was the first time two of their own had been killed. There was no debate, they immediately started planning a reprisal, to equalise the losses. Bastien Vivaldi, in particular, having lost the woman he loved, wanted revenge, and he wanted it rapid. As the days went by, the self-fuelling fury and hatred swelled. Increasingly, and thanks also to the muddled reconstruction of events furnished by a fourth member of the command who had witnessed the scene from outside, the idea began to form that it had been to all intents and purposes a cold-blooded execution. No one bothered to check the facts, being 'overwhelmed by the desire for action', as Mure Galiani would later say. Having given up, for technical reasons, on the idea of attacking particularly conspicuous targets, one of the lads from the squads and another member of Front Line were entrusted with picking the appropriate location: they eventually settled on a wine bar in Via Millio, in Borgo San Paolo. At one o'clock in the afternoon on 9 March 1979, a Friday of lacklustre, hazy sunshine, a stolen Fiat 131 parked up not far from the bar. Five people got out, including Vivaldi, Mure Galiani and his girlfriend: nom de guerre, Laura. They were holding cardboard patisserie trays wrapped in shiny paper; and under that paper there were Kalashnikovs. They walked in, tied the proprietors up in the back room, and then Bastien Vivaldi went over to the bar counter, above which a large mirror loomed saying 'Campari'. He telephoned the police and said he had caught a thief red-handed, stealing his car radio. He said he had immobilised the man and that he would wait for them there, at the wine bar in Via Millio, Via Millio 64/A, right here in the wine bar, he repeated smoothly. More than half an hour went by, and then, finally, a police car reached the bar. The first policeman didn't have time to walk through the door before five bullets went through him. He managed to return fire and then drag himself along the pavement and call out to passers-by for help; and the other policemen who had stayed outside also started shooting; but from behind them shots arrived from the guns held by Laura and the other man, who had taken up position behind a car. Amid the deadly hail of bullets that followed, Laura accidentally hit Galiani in the right arm, forcing him to drop his pistol; he picked up a Kalashnikov and recommenced shooting, using his left hand, despite another bullet having immediately caught him in the knee. By now he was out in the street, leaning on the roof of a car and aiming at a policeman whose pistol was empty and who had taken refuge inside the bar. One of those shots ricocheted and began a journey, a journey which had effectively started forty minutes earlier, when Vivaldi had made his phone call and a bus had left its stop outside a high school to travel across the city, and a boy had then got off that bus, a boy who was almost nineteen and was late for lunch because he had stopped to talk to a teacher who was a great fan of Fenoglio's about the fact that he wanted the subject of the dissertation he had to prepare for his school leaving certificate to be Fenoglio (those minutes, those minutes, those seconds, that dumb bad luck), a boy named Emanuele Iurilli who found himself right in the middle of the shoot-out, and even though they screamed at him to take cover the bullet's journey came to an end inside his right lung and then his liver, which exploded, and the boy hit the ground. The hit squad fled, with Mure Galiani limping, and after hours of circling around they managed to find a safe house where a doctor came to visit him and stopped the haemorrhage but said he wasn't equipped to do anything else for a wound of that kind. The doctor was probably L.B. and, according to the prosecution, the fact that Kim – Kim from the Barabba club, the commander of the patrol groups – had gone to find *him* in particular indicated that he had already volunteered to treat members of Front Line. He said, on the contrary, that up until the very last minute he had had no idea who it was they were taking him to see. I wonder what he did when he came out of that flat, when Kim took him back somewhere and left him there alone. How did he feel? Did his mouth taste rancid? Did he walk alone through the now-soundless city trying to catch his breath, trying to understand, trying to factorise his own feelings into intelligible fractions? And what did he feel when he finally heard about the boy? Mure Galiani was taken over to Milan and received treatment. And the killing of Emanuele Iurilli plunged like a falling reinforced concrete bridge, collapsing itself and Front Line.

But, however incredible it might seem, there is still a third and final scene to come. Vivaldi did not feel avenged; the ambush had been a failure: neither of the policemen had died, and they had managed to kill an innocent boy. Not even that random death had doused their unquenchable hatred; the organisation increasingly resembled a gang of mobsters who felt honour bound to take out all informers, grasses and spies. And the first of the grasses, the original culprit for all this, must surely have been the proprietor of the bar where Vivaldi, Barbara and Matteo had had coffee on the day, back in February, when the police had arrived; it must have been him who telephoned: it was obvious. The tobacconist never occurred to them. They didn't even do their routine checks. The raid would be called 'Operation Judas'. At the time the first shoot-out took place, however, negotiations had been underway for the sale of the bar, and the owner now wasn't even the same person. The new proprietor was called Carmine Civitate. On 18 July, four men in mechanics' overalls walked into the bar. Civitate's wife was standing behind the counter on her own. They ordered liqueurs and waited. Then Civitate came in holding a tray, he put it down on the counter, and a split second later Bastien Vivaldi fired seven bullets into him, the entire contents of the .357's cylinder, which blew open his head and perforated his chest. His wife ran into the back to hide and the terrorists ran off. To the very last they refused to believe they had yet again killed someone who had nothing to do with any of it. They said it was all propaganda designed to stain the organisation's reputation; they wrote feverish bulletins in which they threatened to identify and punish anyone who dared do anything like that (we can kill everyone, and we will kill everyone ...). At the trial, in 1983, the tobacconist took the stand and testified that it had been him who had telephoned the police on that long-ago day. Behind the bars of the dock, a stony silence fell over the defendants.

After much hemming and hawing, I decided I would also look out Mure Galiani. Agata maintained that L.B. had never examined or treated him; from the grounds of appeal it resulted that he had. Mure Galiani, Front Line's military commander-in-chief, member of the national directorate, personally responsible for four murders, sentenced to life in jail and then, by the court of appeal, to twenty-nine years, a supergrass in the 1980s. Finding his contact details turned out to be surprisingly easy. When I told my mother that I was planning to write to him, she, who was normally so phlegmatic, hit the roof.

'*Those* people are not the people you should be speaking to,' she shouted down the phone. 'You don't need to ask *him* about it. And how would it help you, to know if it did or didn't happen? What would it change?'

It was a good question. Why did I need to know? The grounds of appeal presented it as an established fact. So it had happened. It was something L.B. had clearly accepted responsibility for, while refusing to see it as an act of collusion, let alone active participation. Did I want absolute certainty? Perhaps. Or perhaps it was something more convoluted: on the one hand that ferocious desire to salvage another piece of my father, even from within that ungodly, alien world which I would never have another opportunity to access; and also, yet again, I realised, the hopeless desire to know what my father had thought, what he had seen, what words he had uttered or had maybe kept to himself – my increasingly powerful angst at that series of places where I would never reach him. And on the other hand, a stranger feeling: there was a part of me that also wanted to verify Mure Galiani's realness. Had it all truly happened? Did he really exist? Was he a living creature, a flesh-and-blood person, and not just an abstract character from the weekday news reports?

'I'd just like to know what happened,' I said. And that was the truth.

'Do what you want,' said my mother after a brief, chilly silence.

But I didn't find out much more than I already knew. And it wasn't an earth-shattering or significant moment. It was all disconcertingly banal, a bit like sending a Christmas card to a distant relative; and all of it was done with impeccable politeness on both sides. I wrote him an email; I told him who I was and what I wanted, apologising for disturbing him and hoping that my request would not reawaken painful memories. Mure Galiani replied very urbanely, explaining that, given the state he had been in at the time of the putative encounter with L.B., it would have been rather difficult to remain lucid enough to have remembered anything. He also said, seraphically, that he didn't find it in the least bit painful to talk about these things, that he had now reached 'the age of recollection' (that *in the least bit* angered me). He then spoke to another former Front Liner – Kim, as it happens – who instead had very clear recollections of L.B. and of that particular day, and a week later Galiani wrote me another email, saying that he owed a 'debt of honour' to my father and by extension to me. The choice of expression was one I found striking (it was so alien to me, to any ethos I had, so alien to my way of thinking), as was the fact that he now referred to my father as Him, with a capital H. The two of us were clearly never going to be speaking the same language.

It had been Kim, as I already knew from the prosecution material, who had gone to fetch L.B. to give Galiani urgent medical care. What L.B. did for him, Mure Galiani wrote, he had already done for other people who had been wounded in skirmishes following street protests. Asking no questions and without knowing who he was. In the name of 'professional ethics and solidarity'. Then he added some things I already knew: that L.B. had not participated in any way in Front Line, that in prison he had acquitted himself admirably (I'm not sure what he meant by that), that – he had been told – L.B. had studied for a law degree while in prison and, in court, had steadfastly denied belonging to Front Line, which was the truth, but he was convicted anyway. 'During the years of the counterterrorism state of emergency, they didn't split hairs,' he concluded.

He asked me to put a flower on my father's grave for him. I didn't tell him that my father's ashes had been scattered at sea and I couldn't very well take flowers there. And that perhaps I wouldn't have, even if I could have. He had been very obliging, after all.

And that was all there was to it. I had obtained something. But without knowing why, I still felt I had been left emptyhanded. I had been left standing, disorientated, on an empty strip of land.

From 1979 one happier image has, in any case, survived. It was Alberto and Lucilla who described it to me, and they, too, brought me photographs. They had, they told me, all gone up to the Venice film festival, and had pitched their tents outside the Palazzo del Cinema on the seafront. In the photos L.B. was wearing a blue waistcoat, and was always squinting into the sun, and didn't ever seem capable of standing still, not even when the others were sitting on the steps enjoying the sunshine. He stood with his hands on his hips, or was sauntering around somewhere nearby.

They didn't have passes, so they went to see the films being shown at two or three o'clock in the morning. They accidentally saw *The Empire Strikes Back* in English with French subtitles. That made me laugh.

'We weren't especially keen to see it,' Alberto smiled, 'but it was fun.'

Meanwhile, back at the Factory, a strange thing happened that October. Out of the blue, sixty-one workers received letters of dismissal which were very generic and all exactly the same: they were accused of having performed their duties unsatisfactorily and of adopting a demeanour inappropriate in the workplace. The rest of the workforce immediately downed tools; the head of the General Italian Confederation of Labour announced that before taking any form of action he would wait to be informed of the motivations behind the dismissals. Essentially, the sixty-one were accused of stoking tensions inside the Factory, with serious repercussions in terms of productivity; but, and above all, there was also an insinuation that some form of propinquity with terrorism was involved. Talk – and all of their energies – focused on violence at the factories and during protests, which forms of combat were legitimate or unjustifiable, the appeals put in by the workers who had been sacked. No one noticed that, with this unforeseen move, the Factory had opened hostilities: they were all too busy demonstrating that productivity was key for them too, and that they, too, felt that violent troublemakers should be removed – in spite of the fact that nearly all of the dismissed workers won their appeal and only four of them turned out to have links of any kind with the Red Brigades. The Factory had run an experiment, as part of ongoing preparations for the 'restructuring' of which there had been talk for some time but the nature of which nobody had yet grasped: they had driven in a wedge, and it had worked. Had anyone been observing more carefully, they might have interpreted that strange episode as a presage; a small black streak of tar on the road, pointing to something in the future.

On 11 December Front Line stormed the SAA, the School of Business Administration, which held courses designed to put students in touch with employers. The previous year the school had also launched an MBA programme, which represented – and not just symbolically – something that needed to be destroyed at the earliest possible opportunity, and ideally in a particularly sensational attack. The assault was planned with meticulous attention to detail. At around a quarter past three in the afternoon, just after lessons began, five well-dressed young people presented themselves unexpectedly, each of them carrying a briefcase. They walked into the lecture theatre, where a lesson was underway. One of them – young, dark, composed – said to the students and the female lecturer sitting on the dais: 'I'm from Front Line. Stay calm and nothing will happen to you. This building is now occupied.' Then he and the others opened their briefcases and pulled out their weapons. In came another man, carrying a gym bag; he pulled out a submachine gun.

Outside, at the main entrance and in the car park, there were seven more of them covering the exits, all wearing bullet-proof vests under Loden coats and anoraks. But there must have been others, because they combed the classrooms, bar and library and rounded them all, students, lecturers and secretarial staff – almost two hundred people – into the main lecture hall. The ritual homily was given: a young woman who seemed less calm than the others, and whose voice sounded jittery and tense, explained to the students that here at the SAA they were being schooled as managers for multinationals, and that they should abandon their studies or else. Someone protested and was hushed. It was all explained, said the Front Liners, in the leaflet.

R.R., Front Line's intellectual, consulted the list of teaching staff and set about selecting the right lecturers: four of them were managers from the Factory, one from Olivetti. They asked to see ID cards to make sure, and asked a few questions. One of the managers had been working on production plans at the Factory together with the engineer Front Line had killed back in September, and he was immediately selected as one of the chosen five. The five students were instead picked at random. Ten. And afterwards nobody would fail to grasp the implications of that number. In the lecture hall everyone was forced to crouch down with their heads between their knees and eyes glued to the floor, even though the terrorists were all unmasked. But even at this stage the accounts vary: some people reported being forced to lie face-down on the floor. Each of them, as always happens, lived their own version of that terror.

Some of the chosen ten were taken out to the toilets and some to the corridor outside the toilets. And here again, and even more markedly, accounts varied. Five against one wall and five against the other, or perhaps they were in two different areas. Some of them were tied up and silenced with strips of parcel tape across their mouths; but not all of them. In any case, there was a form of ritual. In one of the versions, after having talked about 'Carla and Charlie' and the multinationals, four of the terrorists pointed guns at their victims; then, with a deliberate unhurriedness, they stared at each of them, grim-eyed, as if imprinting an indelible loathing and contempt. Finally, they shot them in the legs, one by one. One lecturer remembered the pistol being pointed at his face. In another version, they made them turn to face the wall, they talked about their murdered comrades and all the rest of it; and the victims, who had no way of seeing any of it, heard the hissing of the spray can with which they wrote their moniker on the wall, and Barbara and Matteo's aliases. Then two shots in each person's legs, all along the row. An extra bullet was reserved for one of the lecturers because they discovered he had a licence to carry firearms, and self-defence by the dominant class was not acceptable. The last one left waiting, a student who just a few minutes earlier had been writing Christmas cards while waiting for a lesson to begin, lost all sense of time as he listened to the shots getting closer and felt the bodies slumping without a murmur because their mouths were taped shut; and in those few split seconds he also lost the most basic of animal instincts, the will to live: he just wanted it to be over, over, it didn't matter how; and he discovered with relief that if they shoot you at very close quarters the pain is less intense. He was the one most badly wounded, disabled for life at thirty-three.

There is no one official version of how events unfolded on 11 December 1979 at the SAA All of them differ, even if only in some small detail. Reading them back to back, the feeling is that what we have before us is a sort of compendium of traumatic recollection – the most untrustworthy kind of all. But it is interesting to note that, when interviewed the very next day, and while recalling the terrorists' incongruous courtesy, all of the wounded said that they could not remember the terrorists' faces, and many of them had already forgotten the exact order in which things were done and said. And all of them insisted on those blanked-out faces, which in all probability they had seen well and up close, but the features had atomised and dissolved a second later, as though engulfed by the surge in their brains. Of the people who shot them, all that remained was a throbbing echo.

One professor who was in the lecture theatre together with the others explained to *L'Espresso* that: 'I was kneeling on the floor with my head between my knees approximately thirty-five years ago, and someone else was pointing the machine gun at my back. The Nazis. Back then I was a boy, today I'm a grown man, but this situation is identical. The same methods the Nazis used, the same courteous Prussian formality, the same cold eyes. Murderers' eyes.'

(Many of those who survived attacks by Front Line and by the others have mentioned those eyes. One witness – I don't remember who – said that one of them, walking towards her, or towards her boyfriend whom he was about to shoot, had smiled, but only 'with the lower half of his face'. Those eyes didn't smile.)

The terrorists made their getaway from the business school and released their usual statement. The butchery was over. In all, it had lasted half an hour. A lake of blood spread its way out along the corridors, together with the screams and whimpers. But had there really been screams and whimpers? Other people remember silence. Because of their mouths being sealed with tape. When, finally, someone managed to get to their feet and leave the lecture theatre in search of help, he skated and slid and crawled across the blood on his hands and knees. The first members of the emergency services to arrive splashed up blood as they walked in, as though their feet were landing in puddles deep with a day's worth of rain. If there had been silence, it finished now. The screams – and it was no longer even clear where they were coming from – went on and on and on, and seemed to spread right through the city.

The closer my father's time got to my own, the more he seemed to elude me, the more the blanks seemed to multiply. But at that point, the fact that I was *still* younger than him, that I *still* hadn't reached the age at which certain things had happened to him, made him feel extraordinarily alive; it sheltered me from the future and crystallised his past: there were things that hadn't happened to him yet. His youth was expanding, and so was mine.

Years had now gone by since all of this began, but I still pined for the ghostly years in Rome, which remained perhaps the most substantial lacuna in the whole story, because I had never yet met anyone else who had been there with him. And then a wonderful thing happened. Alberto, L.B.'s friend from the PCIM-L who had never stopped trying to help me and had never stopped looking for useful contacts (it was he who put me in touch with Druina, for example), wrote to me one day saying that someone he knew had a friend in Rome who might have known L.B.

'Clara,' he wrote. 'Does it mean anything to you?'

You bet it meant something to me! I covered my face with my hands and sobbed. Here she was, Clara *disparue*, the long-lost sweetheart, the girl from the bourgeois family, for the love of whom L.B. had staged an improvised protest in the courtyard, the only person who had witnessed Rome! And she was being returned to me ... The day we spoke on the phone it was raining, and the phone kept cutting off, and she was another one of those people who never remember anything, but she did remember him being fun, and she remembered them helping out at the after-school clubs together, out in the poorer suburbs, and how important they felt it was to be there with those children, and that they hardly ever saw one another because they were always dashing backwards and forwards, and they barely had time to kiss because they were so busy, and that she often got angry with L.B. because he told her his inveterate pointless lies, he would tell her he was going somewhere and then she would run into him somewhere else, but without there being a motive, without there being anything nasty to it, just like always, as if he couldn't help himself, even back then. Clara also sent me a very precious photo: L.B. in 1968, very young and beardless, wearing a duffel coat, giving an impassioned speech on a little dais in front of the university, surrounded by other young people who had climbed up on to the dais, in front of a big crowd of students.

The sensation was one I had only ever felt once before, one evening when, while I was distractedly watching a documentary, they had shown images of 16 March, the day when the neo-fascists had been at the university and had thrown desks and chairs out of the windows, images I had already seen and searched for a particular face seen dozens of times before, and suddenly – who knows why I hadn't ever noticed him, how it was possible, but perhaps it was because I now had the picture Agata had given me of him as a young man – suddenly, as I was saying, I leapt to my feet and nearly knocked my plate flying, because I *had seen him*. It was blurry, he was distant, it really was just a few fractions of a second, but it was *him*. Something hit him, he slumped to the ground off-screen, two friends lifted him to his feet and, holding him by his arms, they rushed him down the stairway, while, with the face of someone in pain, he held his head in his hands. I abandoned my supper and looked for those images online, and I watched them, I re-watched them, I found that face, and it really was him. It hadn't been a hallucination.

I don't know why I found that short film clip quite so moving. I think, perhaps, it was because, after all those other people's words and memories, it was the first physical evidence I had of something that had happened to him. Historical proof. Now I knew for certain that L.B. had really existed.

For 1980, I only have two images. The first is from after the thirty-five-day strike that started on 10 September, when the Factory announced that fourteen thousand four hundred and sixty-nine people were being made redundant, and the workers understood that this was now no longer a battle but war; and for thirty-five days they downed tools in all the factories and marched through the streets and flocked together to shed tears and to quarrel in endless assemblies, and camped out at the gates of the Factory's main plant, and at night the fires lit by the picketers burned away in the dark like the cheerless little campfires of a last surviving trench; and in the end, after an unusual protest march made up of managers and white-collar workers who demanded that the Factory be reopened and asked to return to work, a march which the cynical suspected had been orchestrated from above, an agreement was reached between the company and the unions, according to which a certain number of furloughed workers would be reinstated. But that agreement was never respected; and, on the last of those thirty-five days, a group of workers, the remaining few, marched from Mirafiori into the city centre anyway, in silence, perfectly well aware that they had been defeated by history; but they marched all the same, as if by way of wordless explanation, and in the middle of it all, walking in silence, dripping with rain, L.B. was there too, with Sebastiano, his old comrade, Roberto's friend, the one who had been at Strada delle Cacce with him. They said nothing to each other, and when it was all over, they separated with a quick, sad embrace.

The second image is one Emanuele Pariante had supplied me with when I went to speak to him. L.B.'s former comrade in the PCIM-L, the one who then went to America. He was now living and working in a pretty little house with a loft-style mezzanine floor in Borgo Campidoglio, one of the quirkier areas of Turin, a little village in the middle of the city, a neighbourhood which had previously been working class, with narrow streets and small houses. His had a vegetable patch and a garden, and he was waiting outside, terribly thin beneath a shirt and trousers which hung off him, and he was in a very good mood, as was his girlfriend who had a magnificently impish face, voluminous black hair and blue eyes. She sat down to work at a table behind us and intervened only once, to tell me that she had met L.B., not in connection with Pariante, but years before the two of them got together, at the end of the 1970s, and that she still had very fond memories of him; she told me that, for a while, he had looked after a girl who had mental health problems. One day, possibly under the effects of something psychoactive, the girl had fallen from a balcony. And he kept dropping by to see her in hospital, to check she was improving, until she was fully on the mend.

Pariante instead told me about the PCIM-L and the fact that he and L.B. had always been kept slightly on the sidelines, and he described the ins and outs of L.B.'s experience of the party, and Strada delle Cacce. He hadn't known that L.B. had been arrested for membership of an armed band in 1982; that caught him by surprise. The last time he had seen L.B., he told me, was when he came back from the United States in 1980, and there was that earthquake in Irpinia. The following morning, at dawn, they had found themselves on the same Red Cross truck, which was carrying volunteers down from Turin. It had been at least five years since they had last seen one another. L.B. didn't seem to have changed, he was just a bit tireder than normal. Misa had lent him a blue overcoat because he didn't have one that was warm enough. Agata's brother was there with them, too.

Many hours later they arrived in that devastated, unreal land, which was covered with rubble as far as the eye could see, and with people running, carrying bodies, with no electricity, running water or phone lines any more. And then it started snowing. They were there for quite some time, said Pariante. Weeks, maybe a month, perhaps even longer. L.B. worked in a field tent, where he and other doctors tried to offer the wounded some immediate help and comfort, and the wounded continued arriving, for days and days. After having helped dig people out or pull the bodies free, Pariante and Agata's brother took a truck and went off, every day, in pursuit of the looters who were stealing from homes that had collapsed. There was a dreamlike atmosphere in that ruined place, silent now and inert, muffled by the snow which entombed everything: the church towers, the buildings, the indifferent mountains.

Once, when they were sitting on a doorstep having a moment's break, several weeks after the rescue effort began, L.B. had said to him: 'Down here you get the impression winter could go on for ever. Like a magic spell, putting time on hold.'

'It sounds almost as if you like the idea,' remarked Pariante.

L.B. didn't reply.

'Ah, but do tell me a bit about this trial of his. I knew nothing about it, seriously,' said Pariante, moving his cigarette absent-mindedly. 'What happened?'

I gave him a brief summary, and I also told him what had happened afterwards. He listened to me with his eyes screwed up and then smiled sardonically.

'But why do you want to tell this story? What is this? Some sort of Puglian thing about payback? Are you trying to clear your father's name?'

His girlfriend lifted her head and threw him a filthy look. I stiffened and put down the pen I had been taking notes with.

'No,' I said.

It wasn't the first time someone had asked me why. And all of them tried to find an explanation of some sort. I couldn't see why they felt it was so important. All those psychoanalytical explanations: it was an act of forgiveness, of reconciliation, some sort of attempt to redeem the 'good' communists, an apologia in defence of my father, an essay, of a sort, on the 1970s – that kind of thing. Pariante's was hands-down the most idiotic thing anyone had ever said to me. None of them ever considered the most straightforward explanation of all: that it was simply an act of interest.

Pariante studied me for a moment, as though trying to establish whether or not I was telling the truth, then his gaze wandered off again, meditatively.

'You know ... Leonardo lived the life he wanted to. He was always where he wanted to be, all things considered. He carried on practising democracy when no one gave a fig about being democratic any more, when no one any longer gave a fig about anything at all. It was a life cut short, in a certain sense, unfinished. But it was what the English would call "a decent life". I can't think how to put that any better in Italian. And that, it seems to me, is the thing that counts.'

He put his cigarette out and blinked a couple of times.

'Do come back to see us. We're always here, at the bottom of the garden.'

In desolate cities, the parting shots continued to arrive, from Front Line, from the Red Brigades and their emulators, or from those who had deserted the original organisations and had set up new ones. The only thing anyone could do was circle the wagons and attempt to dissuade anybody likely to fall prey to the armed bands, before they got roped in. L.B. who, like thousands of others, was furloughed in September 1980, would spend months of his life doing just that. If someone they knew of was arrested, and especially if the charges were meaningless or unjust, they endeavoured to help them out financially and, every now and then, at least, get decent food to them – better than the prison food; or they made sure their homes were kept clean: little things of that kind – practical, essential. L.B., like a preacher, went into the factory districts where the youngsters were, where people were more at risk, and he tried to explain to them that Front Line was a dead end and that if they got caught up in terrorism they would be sacrificing their youth, their future, everything. And all of this was engulfed in a dirty white blanket of heroin.

The anti-repression committee was still very busy, especially now that, in the wake of the Dozier case (the American general kidnapped by the Red Brigades and freed partly thanks to information wrested from the terrorists by violent means), some of the forms of torture being used had become public knowledge – the truncheons in vaginas, the salt water, the beating of genitals, the pincers pulling at nipples, the strippings and humiliation, the heads thrust underwater, the simulated drownings, the punches alternating with mellifluous questions. One high-ranking police officer was widely known as De Tormentis.

Although, the committee had grey areas of its own. And not just the committee. When Patrizio P. – the Red Brigade column leader who would agree to collaborate with the investigating authorities – was arrested in the piazza near my home, the era of the supergrasses had begun. They called them '*pentiti*': repenters. The fact that reduced sentences were on offer encouraged numerous detainees, both notorious and insignificant, to talk, to identify hideouts, to name names, to explain dynamics which had until then remained obscure. The *pentiti* were actually seen as traitors by nearly all of the extra-parliamentary left wing. Traitors to their own comrades, the lowest of the low; even if those comrades were mass murderers. And then there were cases of *pentiti* who, having been thrust into that perverse system of carrots and sticks, pointed the finger at people who had done nothing wrong. Of course, there were also *pentiti* like Roberto Celauro, a man bordering on the psychopathic, who, the minute he was arrested, had rattled off lists of all the operations and all the names, in that calm, pedantic little voice of his, scrupulously precise and with an extraordinary memory (he liked specifying which weapons had been used, he loved guns and apparently found remembering the murders a pleasurable experience). And he was well aware that he would be rewarded for it. He, who had killed, would serve a lighter sentence, for example, than a girl who had never so much as picked up a pistol – and that was what the critics contested and claimed to find so twisted. And in effect there was something twisted in it. Celauro – whom his comrades, for motives perhaps not incomprehensible, knew as 'Crazy Roby' – would have a curious career: in the 1990s he ended up joining the right-wing, secessionist Northern League, was expelled, was arrested again – for having attempted to plant bombs in one or more mosques – and would die in prison a few days after my first encounter with the grounds of appeal.

There were certainly many opportunists, but also, perhaps, a few people with more complex motivations: the beginnings of a crisis of conscience, some terrible doubt that suddenly flared up in their minds; and also, perhaps – and some of them said so openly – the desire to put a stop to it all, knowing that the turn things had taken could lead only to all-out catastrophe.

But, in general, the attitude towards them, even on the part of people who had never belonged to any of the armed groups, was contemptuous almost to the point of repugnance.

In any case, the atmosphere within the committee was starting to become unpleasant, especially – since a good proportion of the initial cohort of workers had left some time back – with all the new arrivals. In the end, even Petra left. She could no longer stand the ambiguity. She did not think the assassins were 'comrades who had slipped up', although she did understand how important it was not to let their guard down with regard to the prisons question. She simply didn't consider them comrades: she thought they were something other than that, although she couldn't say exactly what. So, with great sadness, she left that committee which had been like a family to her, and even if her friendship with L.B. came to an end for political reasons when she chose another path, she would always remember him (and greet him, if they ever bumped into each other) with great joy. Over the phone, in that still-soft voice of hers, she told me that everything she knew about politics she had learned from him. And she still spoke lovingly of her little girl's 'papo'.

There was nothing left. Nothing. Oh, there were still the workers' assemblies, but they seemed meaningless. The words they used had lost their referents. Like the word 'comrades', for example. They were empty, desiccated, the shell of an insect left on a wall in the sun. The dead, fossilised language of the chimera appeared to have triumphed, even if all of its leaders were in prison now, often ushered there by the confessions of the 'traitors'. A dead language in a dead city.

The 'traitors' were assassinated one after another. William Waccher – a lad who had only ever distributed leaflets for Front Line and, after being arrested, had, in his terror, blurted out names – was freed in February 1980 and, at Porta Ticinese in Milan, found a commando group waiting to punish him. Patrizio P.'s brother was killed following a terrifying 'proletarian trial', which was filmed in front of the flag with the five-pointed star, with the 'Internationale' playing drearily in the background. His face, when they pronounced him guilty. His face! The body was found near the Capanelle racecourse in Rome, riddled with eleven bullet wounds. In December 1981, Giorgio Soldati, a Front Line militant who had collaborated with the authorities over a triviality (a cache of explosive material that he himself had buried and which was now so degraded as to be unusable), was 'tried' in prison, in a trial which those present all remember being one of the most unsavoury things they had ever witnessed. And – even though he was supposed to have been in solitary confinement – he was, when it finished, strangled in the refectory. The room's peepholes had all been obstructed, but the guards obviously hadn't noticed. One young man from the working-class suburbs held out for nine days while being tortured; and then he talked: but in the time he had bought for the others to get themselves organised and escape they had not cleared out all of the hideouts, and they moved too slowly, and some of them were arrested. And so he was punished. The *snitch*. He was killed in July 1982, during the recreation hour at the super-maximum security prison in Trani.

And yet 1982 seemed to bring a glimmer of hope. Things began moving, slowly, in the city. There were citizens' assemblies; evenings of music were organised, timidly, to draw people out of the houses they had been barricaded into for years. In January L.B. was contacted by Colomba, whom he had met back in the Materferro days and had continued to see above all because one of the man's children was sickly and L.B. was looking after him. Colomba suggested meeting up in a bar in Via Monginevro – together with a woman whom L.B. immediately recognised as 'one of them' – to arrange the infamous journey to Rome to treat the wounded comrade Mancini. The same Mancini who, two years earlier, had – among other things – shot an architect who designed prisons, holding his head down over the sink; he survived but would spend the rest of his life with a bullet in his neck. Some years afterwards, she tried writing to the architect from prison – whether it was an attempt to establish a dialogue or to ask forgiveness, I don't know. And he agreed to correspond with her and even to meet, hoping to understand. But at the end of a letter he never sent, he concluded that those meetings had been pointless, because he had understood that there was nothing to understand. The architect had been looking for an ideal behind the violence which had engulfed him, behind the pain he had lived with, but there wasn't one: she and her comrades had no ideals, it was just violence; they were prisoners more to that than they were to the fact that they were literally prisoners. And so he never would be offered any clarity, or consolation for the fact that one day someone had pushed his head into a sink and had shot him; or rather: he now knew it had happened *for no good reason.*

In the bar, Colomba wittered on and on, slightly hysterically. The woman was dry and matter-of-fact. As they left, L.B. said to Colomba that he wasn't very convinced. Then, that afternoon, according to the grounds of appeal and as we have known from the beginning, he decided not to go and said that as far as he was concerned Front Line was just ridiculous. He had other things on his mind. The Movement, Misa and Ester had told me, appeared to be regaining vigour that spring; and he was someone people listened to, someone whose lead they followed. He had reacquired his enthusiasm. On 6 June 1982, a big and very well-attended national workers' assembly was held at the Teatro Cinema Giardino, in the course of which L.B. gave a long speech and the armed and non-armed factions finally, definitively, parted ways. Of course, they also discussed government repression and the gradual, comprehensive nullification of the left-wing avant-gardes; and they talked about the prisons; but above all they discussed the absolute necessity of putting the past behind them – without, it goes without saying, abandoning the proletarian detainees – the need to build a new life, the need to look to the future.

On 22 June, L.B. was arrested for participation in an armed band.

We will never know if Colomba gave them his name because, in their eagerness to rid themselves once and for all of that annoying rabble-rouser, the investigating authorities had elegantly goaded him into it, or whether it was because, since everyone had already been arrested, he really didn't have any other names to give them and, in the throes of his distress, named the only person who came to mind. All we know for sure is that they turned up in the morning and arrested L.B., even pointing a pistol at Agata's head, and they turned over the little flat in search of weapons and compromising material which weren't there to be found. From what I was told by a person who prefers to remain anonymous, there was a line-up. Colomba spent the whole of it repeating in a monotone, 'Let him go, let him go, let him go. He hasn't done anything wrong. Let him go, let him go, let him go ...'

L.B. said only that it wasn't Colomba he was pissed off with (L.B.'s choice of phrasing), but the organisation which had recruited him as a gofer despite knowing that the man was vulnerable. A harmless little fellow, as the lawyer would describe him to me.

Then L.B. disappeared for several weeks. That was routine, under the emergency laws. While an increasingly desperate Agata went from police station to police station asking for news of him, and no one provided her with any, he was in solitary confinement in the underground cells of an unnamed station house. He once said to me, 'You have no idea what solitude means,' but he didn't say any more than that. I have forced myself to imagine it: but every picturing I have attempted has seemed such an impoverished version of the reality of a man alone, literally in the dark as to what is to be of him, that I have had to stop there, on the threshold. You have no idea. I have no idea. I can visualise the walls, the bunk, the hole in the floor which is the toilet, the silence, the noises in the distance, the little window; but all I can do is visualise it. I can't imagine the hours, the night, the not knowing when and how this will ever end. Weeks. Seconds minutes hours. Days. Nights. Without a change of clothes. Without a human voice. In almost total darkness, stinking of latrines and your own unwashed body. Without books, without newspapers, without a single thing to occupy the monstrous, dilated, abnormal time. Up there, outside, life goes on, trams screech. There's someone who loves you. They don't know where you are. But the sun comes up and night falls. It's summer, it was summer beforehand, it must still be. Even now.

You have no idea.

Then he went to jail. The *Carceri Le Nuove*, the New Prisons, which is what the complex was called even though it was built in the nineteenth century, replacing all the other places in which criminals used to be incarcerated. It was abandoned at the end of the 1980s, and in the fog, in the winter, in the evening, it looks like a crumbling, reddish, medieval fortress, with its turrets and the ditches which are filled with weeds now, and the subterranean cells where the partisans were kept before being shot, and, later on, the prisoners in solitary confinement. A place filled with ghosts.

L.B. ended up in number six wing.

Finally, Agata was able to see him. They saw each other during the weekly visiting hour, in a tiny little room, with a guard standing behind them. One day, glass barriers were put up – the kind designed to prevent them even touching. L.B. began walking into the room, saw the screens from the door, and said to the guard that he refused to attend visits until those glass panels were removed. He refused her visits for weeks, until they finally gave in and installed glass panels that only separated the tables, and then – who knows why? – towards the end of his time in jail, he and Agata ended up in the big room reserved for ordinary prisoners, normal prisoners, where you sat at a proper table and talked, and you could embrace, and there was the pleasant sound of other people's chatter.

None of his relatives ever came to see him, not even once. Every so often a friend would go, above all Cecilia, who was following the progress of his case from outside. He wrote letters – to Misa, to Ester, to the others who had stuck by him – letters which have almost all been lost in the course of house moves. The letters to Agata still exist. They are very tender. He wrote her detailed descriptions of the way she looked when she came to visit him, as though he had stored up the details to remember in the days that followed – the collar on her blouse, the way she had her hair combed. He spoke of hope – sometimes with those pompous metaphors of his, sometimes with the simple encouragements of a frightened man who wants to reassure his wife. He drew flowers and other little pictures. One time, probably in reply to a letter of hers, or after a visit when she had told him about it, he wrote that he envied her and the girlfriend with whom she had gone to the seaside and to a Chinese restaurant ... 'But do also think about those of us who can't do such things, and are here, going nowhere, and can only dream of the city on the other side of the wall.'

What did he feel, in there, in those empty hours, in the evenings? In that airless cell, when he watched daylight slant through the small window? From there – he wrote in one of his letters – if you climbed on to a chair you could see the rooftops. Did he wonder when he would ever see real daylight again, beyond those walls? Did he ask himself why? Did he think about the fact that out there, in the meantime, human affairs went on? And how bitterly painful was it to think that? He had no idea how long he would remain in there, and that must have been unbearable, agonising. And that city out there, the city he dreamed of. Back-stabbing city! The unintentionally loved and alien city which had, in the end, rejected him; the recondite city that he had never really understood, whom he perhaps never would understand! City who, on certain winter days, when the air is icy and transparent, almost seem carved from your own light! Why have you cast me off, City? Why couldn't I belong to you?

What frames my days? What have I *built*?

He was frightened, too. He knew, although he had nothing to

confess and had named no names, that the fact he had answered their questions without a fuss had affixed an invisible sign to his back. That was the summer the ex-Red Brigadist was murdered in the prison in Trani; and then, in the autumn, there was the frightful case of the two security guards killed simply so that a warning note could be left on their bodies for a particular *pentito*. That episode, strangely, was one he told me about. I don't remember what it was we were discussing, but I do know we were walking across Piazza Vittorio. He had told me the story and then muttered: 'That tells you what point things had got to. *Two people* killed just so that a note could be pinned to them.'

It was almost November when he was finally freed, without any legal motivations that I have been able to uncover – above all because, at that point, his first trial probably hadn't even begun. Agata told me it was a day she would never forget. She had run over to the committee and had joyfully announced: 'Leo's been released!'

Their heads had all whipped round towards her, like snakes. And someone had said, icily: 'So he's talked.'

And so, just as he predicted, L.B. had suddenly become a *'pentito'*. He was out in the cold. One old friend of his (the man who would be present for the conversation I had with the former factory worker who became a teacher, the one who had insisted that my father's story wasn't a downfall) told me (in the course of the same afternoon) that months after the release, perhaps even a year, he had bumped into L.B.; they had greeted one another and had stopped to exchange a few words before going their separate ways. A block further on, an acquaintance of both had appeared from around the corner and had said to him, almost hissing: 'So you speak to Barone? Didn't you know that ...?' And he had made the hand gesture for blabbering. The man walked off with a disapproving grimace. That was what had happened to L.B. It hadn't been jail that destroyed him, as I had initially thought when Agata had told me about the gulf between before and afterwards. It had been his world, turning its back on him.

His political life was over. He no longer had a job. His old 'comrades' (apart from his friends, of course) no longer spoke to him, or they reviled him. He was a broken man.

One day, having sat on the sofa for hours in silence, he suddenly burst into tears. Agata, who had been in a different room, came in and stood there, looking at him, not knowing what to do.

And, between one sob and the next, he said: 'I have wasted my life. I have wasted my life.'

We know more or less how things went after that. We know that he left it all behind, that he wanted to forget it all, and that he pursued the case through the courts until he proved his innocence, that he fell in love with a woman with whom he would have a baby, and that he didn't prove capable of staying with them. In a letter which I reread not long ago, I discovered that he had written (and at the time I hadn't been capable of understanding it): 'When I shut your door behind me, I truly felt I had failed at everything.'

But after that he would live again, and would rebuild himself, and love again, and study again, and much more besides. *A decent life*, as Pariante had said. He still appears in my dreams sometimes, and I ask him for his version, but in my dream he slips away from me, or vanishes. I wonder if he ever thought about the past, about the time before it all came crashing down. Druina said to me that, one time, after I was born, the two of them had met quite by chance, on what was a lovely April day, its golden air full of floating pollen, and had decided to stroll along the river together. They had walked for hours and talked, like old friends do, for hours – among other things about the PCIM-L and those years. To her regret, she didn't remember what he said. But they had been joyful when they said goodbye, squeezing each other's hands.

P., another friend, had told me that, like me, she too had found the funeral unbearable precisely because of that sensation that it had very little to do with the person it should have been celebrating, and at a certain point she had got up and left, even though it hadn't finished yet. Outside, she said, there were a number of people with white hair, each crying alone.

*

I wish it had been him who told me this story. I wish I had had time to hear it. But I do realise that in some sense this book exists because the man no longer does.

In the weeks running up to my thirtieth birthday, something out of the ordinary happened: I began to think about it. I never had attached much importance to how old I was; I had never found the idea of getting older interesting. Possibly because, before then, it hadn't regarded me. The only thing that scared me was the idea of it ending. Not time itself. Time was infinite. Time, as far as I was concerned, was always the same: it had all already happened – even the unendurable things – and all of it had yet to happen. But all of a sudden, my twenties were about to melt away: and for quite a while now I had felt time contracting irrevocably; just a moment earlier it had been October, the leaves had been yellow and red; but actually, as it turns out, here was spring arriving. Time was the blond hair lengthening on the head of S.'s daughter up in Paris, a little girl who hadn't been there a minute ago. It was terrible and miraculous. But – and I knew it – for all that it was getting shorter, frighteningly shorter, time doesn't contract. Time adds itself on to time. The dead are left behind.

One day, during that period, I was walking along a street in Como on my way to work when I had one of those sudden moments of extraordinarily lucid awareness of my own physically present body; and then, immediately afterwards – it was as though an enormous breach had opened up – I found myself thinking about the past and about the time when I had thought of it as an unbroken expanse, and about myself being coinstantaneous and remembering each and every thing and considering none of those memories worthy of note. And all of a sudden, I saw that wasn't true. Every one of those images, every one of those vivid impressions which had washed over me without me knowing what to make of them, without me knowing where to find the key to them, and even the mountains I could see from where I was standing, and the stream and the cherry trees and their bud-covered branches and, in unison, all of those infinitesimal recollections presenting themselves in illogical snatches which I was making a desperate effort to piece together without understanding why, without understanding what their point was, here and now, in connection with me and in connection with the story I was writing: every one of these things was, in reality, part of a single whole; all of those objects, those faint gleamings, all of the beings with whom I had shared a word or a feeling and who appeared to me now, all of them, together, like a truth revealed: this was all me. The stuff of my life was unfurling in front of me, luminous – finally – and distinct, even in its imprecision, as splendid as a dazzling bank of coral from which I would be able to pick off precious pieces and try combining them into new shapes.

Nothing had happened, nothing had changed in the time that had intervened between one footstep and the next, yet suddenly I was seeing very clearly, as though someone had gently slid a pair of glasses I didn't know I needed onto my nose. Now I could appropriate my own experience, and it was a revelation.

And yet, there must have been something – something which had happened recently without me noticing at the time. And then I understood. And beneath the first Kitezh I discovered a second Kitezh: my life. While attempting to piece together my father, I had been obliged to turn around and look backwards, to remember things I believed I already remembered, to try remembering things-erased; I had been forced to examine my past, that past which had seemed a given – integral and perfectly plain to see. And so, inside its exoskeleton, like a great mother-of-pearl-encrusted shell, my father's story contained my own: my story, which I had thought I owned already, and within which, instead, I was uncovering a new plot, a new truth. My real life. Whatever I would end up choosing to make of it.

The trees rustled and I walked on.

It wasn't until a long while afterwards that I finally asked Dora how he had died. He had taken a turn for the worse the day beforehand; he had spent that afternoon with my mother; they had spent a long time talking, with all the fondness of people who have known one another for many years and have put all recriminations behind them.

'He died the death of the wise,' said Dora. We were in the car when she said it, sitting in a car park. 'He had had his eyes closed for a while, and then at a certain point he said, "I'm dying," and I called the nurse, but by the time she got there he'd already gone.'

I stared straight ahead. I did not tell her that this didn't seem to me to be a wise man's death, and that to realise you are dying at the exact moment in which it happens seemed a horrible thing, and that I pitied him so much that I felt like I was suffocating, that I felt as though my head and my body and the windows of the car were foaming with it. But I did not cry in front of her.

He was so angry, while he was dying. And I was angry with him, because he hadn't given me any quarter even now, because he hadn't understood my anguish over Celina's death, because he had lied to me about the real state of his health, and because he was being childishly capricious. Whereas I should have understood him better than anyone else: I was like him. He had been wrong to treat me badly, but I had been wrong too, failing to recognise his wild fear of dying, which was identical to my own. That fear which must have eaten its way through his bones. The same fear that had me recoiling from him and his sickness.

But more than guilt, I feel something else: a singular nostalgia. Not for the past so much as for things that never did happen, things that still hadn't happened, things that would have happened, *maybe*. Nostalgia conjugated in the conditional perfect. Nostalgia for the no-longer-possible. Perhaps one day we would have learned how to communicate. Perhaps, just for once, I would have stroked his cheek.

It was evening and already dark. My father tidied away the supper dishes and picked up a torch. In silence, we slipped on our sandals. There was a tremendous silence outside the house, too; all you could hear was the crickets trilling in the woods. The moon was almost full and splashed her light across the veranda where we ate our meals, and across the tree where Jenny, the English people's daughter, Jenny with whom I always played, used to cling to the branches with her hands and ankles and hang there, swinging over the void. My father set off, turned around to check I was following, and switched on the torch, illuminating the path and the cacti and aromatic shrubs alongside it. The dust made its way into my plastic sandals. We walked for a long time along the track which climbed and dipped between hills that by day were green and rock-strewn and stippled with the pink of bougainvilleas and bushes of golden yellow broom. You could hardly see anything now. The torchlight darted backwards and forwards. We didn't speak. We passed houses with their verandas illuminated, and I know for certain that one of the houses we passed was one of the highest on the island, the house where we had stayed initially, where Harry, a rubicund and kindly Englishman, lived with his girlfriend Gina, a petite Neapolitan lady with orange hair which she always wore up in a ponytail, Gina who welcomed in all the local cats, lame cats, thin cats, cats with one ear missing, and was always surrounded by them whenever she sat on the low wall in front of her house, smoking and laughing her throaty laugh. We may have passed the tumbledown house that Jenny and I and her brother Martin, with his thick red curls and very freckled face, had decided was a witch's house; it was surrounded by nothing but weeds and brambles, and we had competitions to see who would go closest, but we never did go in. We kept going back, though, lured there by the danger, or perhaps by the witch. We passed through the woods, away from the lights of the houses, and I heard the cries of nocturnal birds from somewhere above my head and what seemed to be the leaves sighing damply, and my father was always one or two paces ahead of me but continued to check I was there, keeping the torch lowered so that he didn't dazzle me.

Finally we reached the small piece of higher ground. As we climbed upwards, the silhouette of the island in front of us, the great dark mass of Stromboli, slowly acquired definition against the limpid, open, starry sky, and I caught my breath. We stopped and stood side by side and my father switched off the torch and slipped it into the pocket of his shorts. The volcano had begun erupting that afternoon. We had come to see it.

The rivulets of lava made their way down from the craters at the peak like very slow rivers of amber and scarlet. Every so often, lapilli flew upwards in fountains of sparks. There was no sound, not even a crackle. The sea was dark, except for the light from the occasional boat crossing it. A deep petrol black.

Neither of us moved, neither of us spoke. The silence, which had already felt immense, seemed to have expanded now, to be enveloping everything. Although, if I strained my ears, I could hear something in the background: a low, dull sound, like a rumble or a vibration, which seemed to be rising from the bowels of the earth, from where the earth began. We watched the volcano for a very long time, a time that, to me, felt endless, numbing, as though it might perhaps have lasted all the way through until morning. Like that feeling I had sometimes at night, in the city, when I couldn't sleep and had no idea what time it was because I didn't want to look at the alarm clock, and I could hear the passing cars and no longer knew whether they were the last cars of the night or the first cars of the morning, and that lonely sound was so puzzlingly poignant. In some ways it was the same thing I would feel later on – again on nights when I couldn't sleep – at Dora's holiday home, when I would let myself out on to the balcony at two or three o'clock in the morning and sit, in my nightdress, at the little table, and watch the empty landscape on the other side of the complex – a vast, flat stretch of weeds and abandoned objects beyond which you could see the mountains and sometimes a forest fire burning on one of their peaks, a fire that I knew human beings had lit, and the smoke rose into the sky for miles; and through that emptiness the railway line ran, and now and then a night train went past and gave a feral shriek which reached the balcony where a little girl sat, alone and sleepless, watching. It went past so fast as it shrieked, and my head spun to think of how many people, how many lives sat behind its dark windows. Because – and although I didn't fully understand it yet – within me, outside me, all around me, I sensed the plaintiveness of enormity expanding.

And in front of the volcano, in the night, I felt the same thing – although I couldn't have put a name to it. I wasn't aware of being tired, or even bored, I was aware only of the yawning sky above me and a faint aroma of sulphur mixing with that of the wildflowers and the salt, which wafted in, now and then, on a gentle breeze. I wasn't thinking about anything. I was simply present in my body.

I was with my father on the little piece of higher ground, and we were looking at something unknowable.

Chronology of Key Events

In lieu of translator's notes and in the hope that it will be of help and interest to English-speaking readers, the following is a brief outline of historical events mentioned in *Sunken City*. Where pseudonyms are used in the novel, I have reinstated real names, and I have endeavoured to include only verifiable information – but with an indispensable caveat: 'The *facts*. They won't ever be the facts; you do know that, don't you?'

Julia MacGibbon

1968
Battle of Valle Giulia · Serve the People is founded
The disruption associated with the student revolt of 1967 and 1968 is dramatic but initially nonviolent. Universities across Italy are occupied, including those of Pisa, Turin, Milan, Naples and – at the beginning of February 1968 – Rome.

On 29 February, the Rector of the University of Rome asks the police to intervene and the students are moved out. At 8 o'clock the following morning, approximately 4,000 students gather in Piazza di Spagna, ready to march on and reoccupy the university. They divide themselves into two groups: one makes its way to the main campus, the other to the School of Architecture in nearby Valle Giulia, where 150 policemen are waiting for them. The students charge the police cordon and start throwing eggs and fruit; the police respond with baton charges and tear gas, and call in reinforcements. The students arm themselves with cobblestones and pieces of wood ripped from benches and trees … Newspaper reports will describe what follows as 'full-blown war': several hours of shockingly violent clashes, at the end of which 148 policemen and 478 students are left wounded.

In the autumn of 1968 the protests at Italian universities begin to peter out. The focus of the protest movement shifts from the modernisation of the education system to the concerns of the working class and conditions in Italy's booming factories, particularly in the heavily industrialised north. Student activists set up semi-permanent pickets and begin propagandising at the gates of major factories, most notably at the vast Turin plants of Italy's largest private employer, Fiat.

Innumerable Stalinist and Maoist groups are being formed by student activists. The most notoriously dogmatic of these, the *Unione dei Comunisti Italiani* (*Marxisti-Leninisti*), is founded by Aldo Brandirali on 4 October and publishes the first edition of the newspaper *Servire il Popolo*.

1969
A hot autumn · 'The bomb in the bank'
Between September and December 1969, thirty-two collective bargaining agreements are set to expire in sectors employing four and a half million workers. Growing disenchantment with traditional trade unions – seen as indifferent to the concerns of unskilled and younger workers – has reduced workers' faith in formal negotiations: students and 'workerist' political activists encourage and facilitate direct action both inside and outside the factory gates. The result is semi-spontaneous industrial action on an unprecedented scale: over the course of what is soon labelled the 'Hot Autumn', up to one and a half million people go on

strike; acts of sabotage, go-slows, wildcat walkouts, marches and shop-floor assemblies are the order of the day. The trade union confederations wisely opt to 'ride the tiger' being unleashed, and collaborate with the workers' movement: their recommendation to accept the contract offers made in December 1969 and January 1970 receives almost unanimous support.

On 12 December an explosion rips through the Piazza Fontana branch of the Banca Nazionale dell'Agricoltura in the centre of Milan. Seventeen people are killed, eighty-eight are left wounded. Within the space of an hour, three additional bombs explode in central Rome, injuring fourteen people. On the same afternoon, an unexploded fifth bomb is found in another Milanese bank, in Piazza della Scala, next to the opera house. Left-wing anarchists are immediately arrested. Three days later, one of the men suspected of involvement dies after falling from the fourth-floor window of the police station where he is being questioned.

The Piazza Fontana bombing marks the beginning of what quickly becomes known as the 'strategy of tension', a term first used in print by the British journalists Neal Ascherson, Michael Davie and Frances Cairncross. Writing for the *Observer* on 14 December, they note that many Italians assume the bombings to be the work not of left-wing terrorists but of the ultra-right, somehow in collusion with the centrist political establishment. The suspicion is that, in the face of growing communist influence, a climate of generalised panic is being deliberately created in order to foment distrust of the workers' movement and fear of a communist revolution, thereby encouraging support for moderate centrist governments, or even for a shift towards right-wing authoritarianism. It eventually emerges that the bombs had in fact been planted by neo-fascist terrorists belonging to a group known as *Ordine Nuovo* (New Order).

1970
The 'Workers' Rights Act' · Birth of the Red Brigades
One of a series of reform laws enacted in response to pressure

from the Socialist Party and the protests of 1968–69, the Labour Charter (*Statuto dei lavoratori*), which parliament approves on 20 May, introduces radical improvements in blue-collar workers' rights. These include health and safety in the workplace, the right to unionise and the right to reinstatement in cases of wrongful dismissal. Workers can no longer legally be discriminated against or dismissed for their political or religious beliefs. It becomes illegal for companies to spy on their employees.

*

In August, a group of radical Marxist-Leninist students form what will become Italy's most infamous and deadly terrorist organisation: the *Brigate Rosse* (Red Brigades). Their first attacks on 'the imperialist State of the multinationals' involve arson and kidnappings, targeting factories and senior managers in Milan and Turin.

1972
Serve the People attempts to become a parliamentary party
In April, the *Unione dei Comunisti Italiani (Marxisti-Leninisti)* renames itself the *Partito Comunista (Marxista-Leninista) Italiano* and, a month later, fields candidates in the general election. The party receives a total of 86,000 votes and wins no seats.

1974
'The second bomb, in the piazza in Brescia. And the third one'
On 28 May, a bomb is placed in a litter bin in Piazza della Loggia in the centre of Brescia. It explodes a few minutes after 10 a.m., during a well-attended anti-fascist rally at which trade union leaders and members of parliament are present. Eight people are killed and 102 are injured. Forty-one years later, two members of *Ordine Nuovo* will finally be found guilty of having organised the attack; one of the two men is a former secret service informant. The judges note that *Ordine Nuovo*, 'Were able to count on support if not outright protection from members of the State apparatus and national and foreign security services.'

Early on 4 August, carriage number 5 of the Italicus Express – a night train en route from Rome to Munich – explodes as the train reaches the end of a tunnel passing under the Apennines. The train, which is running twenty-three minutes late, should have been passing through Bologna station at the moment in which the bomb goes off. Former (and future) prime minister Aldo Moro – who at this point is Italy's foreign minister – is supposed to be on board, but unexpected official business forces him to delay his journey at the very last minute. Twelve people are killed, forty-eight are injured. The neo-fascist group *Ordine Nero* (Black Order) claim responsibility, boasting: 'We can place bombs anywhere we want, wherever and however we please [...] we will bury democracy beneath a mountain of corpses.' In 1984, a parliamentary committee of inquiry will find direct links between *Ordine Nero* and the anti-communist *Propaganda Due* (P2) masonic lodge.

1975
Emergency measures · Serve the People disbands
On 22 May the Italian parliament approves the notorious *Legge Reale* (named after Oronzo Reale, the Minister of Justice). A repressive emergency measure intended to help combat political terrorism, the law removes nearly all constitutional guarantees for anyone accused of 'crimes against public order'. Police are given almost unlimited power to use firearms in the face of any perceived threat to public security.

In November, the *Partito Comunista (Marxista-Leninista) Italiano* disbands.

1976
Red Brigades on trial · Birth of Front Line
On 17 May, thirteen of the founding members of the Red Brigades go on trial in Turin. The accused immediately dismiss their own lawyers and announce that they will refuse court-appointed legal representation. The trial stalls.

Three weeks later, in Genoa, the Red Brigades commit their first murders, assassinating Procurator General Francesco Coco and his two-man carabinieri escort.

In the autumn of 1976, former members of the extra-parliamentary communist groups *Lotta Continua* (Ongoing Struggle) and *Potere Operaio* (Workers' Power) unite to form a terrorist organisation which will soon start calling itself *Prima Linea* (Front Line). The first attack for which they will claim responsibility takes place on 29 November: a raid on the offices of the Fiat Managers Association in Turin during which the terrorists seize files containing details of the association's members.

1977
Bologna riots · Conference against repression · Murder of Walter Rossi and death of Roberto Crescenzio
On 11 March, violent clashes take place between police and student protesters in Bologna. Twenty-five-year-old medical student and *Lotta Continua* activist Pier Francesco Lorusso throws a Molotov cocktail at a carabinieri truck advancing down Via Irneria. As Lorusso runs off, he is chased and shot dead by the driver of the vehicle. The following day, Prime Minister Giulio Andreotti will remark: 'What happened was normal and inevitable, given the state things are in at the university.' Three days of riots follow.

In what they claim is an act of retaliation for Lorusso's death, on 12 March Front Line assassinate thirty-year-old police brigadier Giuseppe Ciotta. Ciotta is the terrorists' first victim in Turin. It subsequently emerges that he has been involved in the investigations that led to the arrest of the thirteen members of the Red Brigades whose trial is expected to resume shortly.

With the support of the Communist Party-run city council, on 13 March the government sends tanks into the centre of Bologna. On 14 March, all public meetings are banned in Rome.

On 23 September, tens of thousands of young people descend on Bologna for the so-called 'conference against repression', a three-day meeting and colloquium organised by what will come to be known as the 'Movement of '77'.

As September draws to a close, neo-fascist attack squads launch a series of assaults on militant left-wing students in Rome. On 30 September, a group of young activists from *Lotta Continua* hand out leaflets protesting against the previous day's shooting of their nineteen-year-old comrade Elena Pacinelli. They are chased away from the local headquarters of the *Movimento Sociale Italiano* party, and then see an armoured police vehicle moving towards them. It is shielding a group of armed neo-fascist militants who have walked out of the MSI offices. The neo-fascists open fire and twenty-year-old Walter Rossi is shot in the neck. For several minutes, the fifteen or sixteen police officers present lash out at Rossi's friends, preventing them from helping the dying man. His attackers are left free to escape. (They will be arrested later in the day.)

Rossi's death – and the role played by the police – provokes widespread fury. The following day, angry protest marches take place in several cities. In Turin, left-wing demonstrators throw petrol bombs into the Angelo Azzurro (Blue Angel) bar on the corner of Via Po and Via Sant'Ottavio. One of the bar's clients, a young student-worker by the name of Roberto Crescenzio, is horribly burned and dies two days later.

1978
Red Brigades trial resumes · 'Via Fani': the kidnapping and murder of Aldo Moro

After two years of postponements, on 9 March the trial of the Red Brigades' founders finally resumes in Turin. The city is tense and heavily militarised: 4,000 policemen in combat gear patrol the streets; 900 personal protection officers are on duty.

Since the trial first began in 1976, forty unsuccessful attempts have been made to assemble a jury, and police investigators, lawyers and journalists working on the case have been intimidated and assassinated. Those killed include Fulvio Croce, the elderly president of the Turin Bar Association who, in the absence of any other lawyers willing to handle the case, was obliged by law to serve as court-appointed defence counsel. A jury is eventually put together when Adelaide Aglietta, the leader of the Radical Party, happens to be selected for jury service: Aglietta – who is also the first woman ever to lead a parliamentary party in Italy – accepts the summons despite receiving death threats. Her stubborn bravery, and that of a further five jurors, allows the trial to go ahead.

*

In Rome, on the morning of 16 March, the president of Italy's Christian Democrat party, former prime minister Aldo Moro, is on his way to parliament where a vote of confidence has been tabled. The vote is expected to approve the formation of a Christian Democrat-dominated government of national unity, in which – for the very first time – the Italian Communist Party will participate.

One of post-war Italy's great men of state, twice prime minister and, at various points, minister of justice, minister of education and foreign minister, Moro has been a key promotor of a rapprochement thanks to which the ICP has finally been brought into the establishment fold.

At 9 a.m., in Via Mario Fani, a Red Brigade commando unit intercepts the two cars in which Moro and his security detail are travelling. Moro is kidnapped and, after two minutes of furious gunfire, all five of his police bodyguards are left dead. An hour and a quarter later, a Red Brigade spokesman contacts the press, demanding the release of the thirteen Red Brigade members on trial in Turin.

A nationwide manhunt begins. For fifty-five feverish days, the government refuses to negotiate with the terrorists – despite desperate appeals from Moro's family and from Moro himself, who writes dozens of letters to party colleagues, newspapers and the Pope (a personal friend). At lunchtime on 9 May, Moro's body is found in the boot of a red Renault 4 which has been left parked in a side street in the centre of Rome – 300 yards away from the

Christian Democrats' national headquarters, and 200 yards away from the Communist Party headquarters.

1979

Murder of Judge Alessandrini · Carla and Charlie · Front Line's vendettas · Storming of the School of Business Administration

On 29 January, a Front Line hit squad assassinates Judge Emilio Alessandrini in Milan. The terrorists explain that Alessandrini has been chosen as a target because he is a modernising reformist and therefore a champion of institutional democracy.

*

In February, the Italian Communist Party launches a series of initiatives aimed at discouraging support for left-wing terrorism. One of these is a questionnaire put together and distributed by local sections of the ICP in Turin. In response, Front Line decide to target Michele Zaffino, the young head of the ICP's Madonna di Campagna section on the outskirts of Turin. A four-member hit squad is put together and, on 28 February, they arrive at a bar in Piazza Stampalia, apparently looking for Zaffino (one of them has a photograph of him in their pocket). In response to a telephone call made by a local shopkeeper, the police arrive, a shoot-out takes place and two of the terrorists – Barbara Azzaroni ('Carla') and Matteo Caggegi ('Charlie') – are killed.

Front Line seek revenge. On 9 March they prepare an ambush for the police at another bar in Turin, this time in Via Millio. It ends messily: a high school student is caught in the crossfire and dies in the street outside; and Front Line member Bruno Lo Ronga is accidentally shot in the knee and the wrist by his comrade Silveria Russo. On 18 July, Front Line murder the owner of the bar in Piazza Stampalia – mistakenly assumed to have been the person who called the police on 28 February.

On the afternoon of 11 December, Front Line launch a highly symbolic attack on Italy's first ever business school, the University of Turin's School of Management in Via Ventimiglia. Lecturers and students are held hostage for forty-five minutes, and ten people are kneecapped. As a demonstration of Front Line's 'military' strength it is an enormous success, but the fact that innocent students have been targeted provokes particular disgust, even among sympathisers.

1980

'Pentiti' · 'In desolate cities': the Bologna station bomb · 35-day strike · Irpinia · Front Line reach the end of the line

A new law passed on 6 February, the *Legge Cossiga* introduces reduced sentences for terrorists who turn state's witness (*'pentito'*). The first and most notorious of the *pentiti* include Patrizio Peci (Red Brigades), Roberto 'Crazy Roby' Sandalo (Front Line) and one of Sandalo's close friends and colleagues from Front Line, a young man who previously worked as the librarian at the Galileo Ferraris lyceum in Turin. His name is Marco Donat Cattin and he is the son of Italy's Minister for Work and Social Security, the deputy leader of the Christian Democrats.

At 10.25 a.m. on 2 August, a bomb explodes in the second-class waiting room at Bologna Centrale railway station, killing 85 people and injuring 200. It is the deadliest terrorist attack on Italian soil since the Second World War, but no one claims responsibility. Investigations continue for decades (and, at the time of writing, are still ongoing), and eventually establish that the bomb was planted by members of the neo-fascist *Nuclei Armati Rivoluzionari* (Armed Revolutionary Nuclei) with the support of the P2 masonic lodge and members of the secret services.

On 11 September, Fiat announce over 14,000 redundancies. The following day, Fiat's blue-collar workers down tools: work stops in all Fiat plants nationwide. The strike will last thirty-five days. On 27 September, the government falls; Fiat announce that, to avoid further destabilising the nation, the company will do the responsible thing: they suspend the redundancy notices and instead furlough 24,000 workers. Two weeks later, fearful of losing their jobs, an alleged 40,000 of the company's white-collar workers march through Turin protesting *against* the strike. Within hours, trade union leaders reach an agreement with the company. When it is put to the vote, the majority of the unions' blue-collar members reject it outright, but amid chaotic scenes, with white-collar workers and scabs intervening to block the registration of blue-collar votes, the union leaders declare the agreement approved. Twenty-two thousand of the furloughed workers remain unemployed. (An estimated 200 of them subsequently commit suicide.) The Communist Party newspaper, *L'Unità*, implausibly claims, 'Fiat didn't win,' but the workers' movement in Turin has clearly lost what will turn out to be its last great battle.

On 23 November, a magnitude 6.9 earthquake hits the mountainous area of Irpinia in the southern Italian region of Campania, causing 2,914 deaths and leaving 280,000 people homeless. Help is so slow to arrive that three days later the Campania-based newspaper *Il Mattino* runs the headline 'FATE PRESTO' (please hurry), and the President of the Republic, Sandro Pertini, makes a broadcast to the nation, appealing for volunteers.

Thanks to confessions made by captured members of Front Line, in December 1980 165 arrests are made, effectively eviscerating the organisation. The bloody 'Years of Lead' are coming to an end.

Acknowledgements

I want to thank all the people (they know who they are) who have contributed to my research, who have provided me with material and who have told me their stories and my father's story.

Thank you to the Centro Studi Piero Gobetti for allowing me access to the Bianca Guidetti Serra Archive and the available documents held there relative to Leonardo Barone's trial, and for their help with the research.

Thank you to my mother, who has always been there.

Thank you to the friends who have supported me over the years. They know who they are, too. In particular, thank you to Stefania Di Mella and Mattia De Bernardis for their loyalty, advice and affection. And Niccolò, my companion for many years, dear friend, and indispensable prop for nearly all of the period in which this book was being written.

Thank you to Beatrice Masini for having believed in the book.

Further Reading

While writing this book I have consulted many other books and documents. For readers interested in learning something more, a few titles in no particular order:

Michele Ruggiero, Mario Renosio, *Pronto, qui Prima linea*, Edizioni Anordest, 2014.

Andrea Tanturli, *Prima linea. L'altra lotta armata (1974–1981)*, DeriveApprodi, 2018.

Stefano Ferrante, *La Cina non era vicina. 'Servire il popolo' e il maoismo all'italiana*, Sperling & Kupfer, 2008.

Guido Bertagna, Adolfo Ceretti, Claudia Mazzucato (ed.), *Il libro dell'incontro. Vittime e responsabili della lotta armata a confronto*, Il Saggiatore, 2015.

Adelaide Aglietta, *Diario di una giurata popolare al processo delle Brigate rosse*, Lindau, 2009.

Marco Revelli, *Lavorare in Fiat*, Garzanti, 1989.

Luca Rastello, *Piove all'insù*, Bollati Boringhieri, 2006.

Albertino Bonvicini, *Fate la storia senza di me*, a cura di Mirko Capozzoli, add, 2011.

Alberto Gaino, *Il manicomio dei bambini. Storie di istituzionalizzazione*, Edizioni Gruppo Abele, 2017.

Care compagne, cari compagni – lettere a Lotta Continua, edizioni
 Lotta Continua, 1978.
Corrado Stajano, *L'Italia nichilista*, Mondadori, 1982.
Antonio Moresco, *Lettere a nessuno*, Mondadori, 2018.